HOW TO
FIND INNER PEACE
AND
LEARN TO RELAX

HOW TO FIND

Inner Peace

AND

Learn to Relax

by W. H. M. Stover

HAWTHORN BOOKS, INC.
PUBLISHERS / *New York*

Contents

Foreword

For seventeen years as head of the Dale Carnegie Courses in the nation's capital and nearby areas of Maryland, Virginia, and West Virginia, I was in close contact with most of the personality problems known to man.

At the school, we advised and trained thousands of business and government executives and their employees. The majority of these people sought to learn better techniques in speech, salesmanship, memory, and human relations. But regardless of the enrollment aims they advanced, many of them would confess to me that their gravest problem was nervous tension and an inability to relax.

One fact stood out. No level of leadership, no management executive, ever was fully immune to fear, worry, frustration, and tension. No matter how hard-boiled the administrator, or how crusty the military officer, tney all suffered the same tendency toward overemotionalism.

How to relax in a world of tensions is one of contemporary man's greatest problems. This book seeks to provide some practical answers on how to live a more relaxed life in a world of turmoil.

Never has mankind been so insecure. Never have our people been so close to moral bankruptcy. Never have we been so close to a general failure of the human spirit. Hypocritical selfishness and emotional instability combine to produce an empty philosophy of life for today and to hell with tomorrow.

So, after seventeen years, having accumulated a large file of case histories in the area of human behavior— emotional instability, success and failure attitudes, habits, and tendencies—I felt compelled to share what I have learned with others.

There can be no question concerning the need for a simple and realistic approach to the problems of controlling everyday tensions. Had such counsel been available to me in the forties, I might have averted a serious physical problem.

Here are some things that this book is not: It is not academic or technical. It is not a scientific treatise. It involves no hard work, no time-consuming exercises.

It is not a book on self-hypnosis. On the contrary, it teaches and encourages the individual to dehypnotize and free his brain from negative tendencies. It is not psychiatry, although it seeks to eliminate and head off emotional conflicts. It is not physiotherapy, although it deals with muscular relaxation, occupational therapy, and recreational therapy. It is not psychotherapy, although there are many guides on how to avoid or get out of psychological sand traps. It is not a road map or blueprint of when, where, and how to work—or not work—to rest, play, walk, run, sit, or stand.

It is not an attempt to tell any individual when or how much to loaf, where to vacation, or what recreation or amusement is best for him. Individual circumstances are the determining factors.

It is not sophisticated, whatever that term may mean, and it is admittedly replete with formulas and quotes and bromides and clichés. Remember that people are quoted because what they have to say is valuable, and that a cliché only becomes a cliché because it is true.

Instead, this book presents some practical, simple, pleasant approaches to a relaxed life. It emphasizes basic habits, tendencies, traits, and attitudes until they combine and fit together into a relaxed personality.

There is no surefire secret formula that will produce miraculous results overnight. This book does, however, illustrate certain do-it-yourself methods suitable for dealing with nonclinical tension.

It makes no apologies for the fact that it is inspirational in tone and that it accentuates the positive, nor even that its style may be considered old-fashioned; the fact that Christianity is inspirational and positive and is considered old-fashioned in some quarters does not detract one iota from its essential truths. One thing I do know about this book is that it works, just as I know that religion works.

You will find that certain premises are repeated. This is deliberate. Nonclinical tension is a habit—a very bad habit. This book attempts to supplant bad mental habits with good ones, and the reader must be reminded of what he is trying to do as he is shown different ways of doing it. Simplistically, this book shows and illustrates practical methods that will help relieve the tensions of the average American; that will enable him to relax and get more out of the only life he has.

It is not designed for the mentally ill; nor for the person whose tension is so psychotic that he needs psychiatric care. It is meant for you, if you have allowed yourself to channel your energies into the needless and destructive tension habit. Everyday tension is a self-destructive state of mind, an extremely negative attitude. The reverse of the tension coin is relaxation. That, too, is an attitude, a state of mind—but a positive mental attitude, just as tension is a negative attitude and state of mind.

As you read this book you will find some chuckles. You might even be tempted to cry. You may scoff at some parts and get the jolt of self-recognition in others. Read through to the end and you'll return to reread certain parts again.

Think over the message and apply it. You will learn to relax. At first it will be a conscious effort, but as you absorb and apply the lessons you have learned you'll find that relaxation has become a pleasant and unconscious habit that leaves no room for the tension that has needlessly been sapping your productive forces and dragging down your spirit. I know you will be happier. You probably will be healthier. You travel life's road only once. Take full advantage of every precious moment. Relax—and live.

HOW TO
FIND INNER PEACE
AND
LEARN TO RELAX

1

Tension
and Your Need
to Relax

THE FIRST STEP

We live in what is popularly supposed to be a civilized
society, even though from the newspapers and TV and the
events we see in daily urban life we may sometimes wonder. Nevertheless, most urban Americans live in what is
the most civilized of societies. Our civilization has brought
technological advances and a standard of living previ-
ously unknown in world history. It has also brought
pressures and problems upon us that have never before
existed. On a personal and emotional level these pressures have resulted in what is commonly called tension.
In the twentieth century tension is a mental attitude
that makes otherwise happy lives into individual hells.
For far too many, tension brings a constant and unneces-

sary emotional agony. It can also bring on serious illness, and sometimes death.

Tension is a mental and emotional condition, even though it often results in physical distress and illness. To analyze and discuss it fully will require more years of study by psychologists and physicians. Yet all the millions of hours of work in this field in our great universities and medical schools have resulted only in clinical approaches for the psychotic or in generalities that fail to resolve the everyday tension problem for the average individual. For tension *is* individual, and each person must resolve his individual problem for himself. I do not profess to be a professional psychologist, nor do I have any magic wand that will relieve tension for any specific individual.

I do, however, honestly believe that a simple common-sense approach can go far to reduce or eliminate your tensions, and I want to share with you what I have learned. There is an old saying that the lawyer who takes his own case has a fool for a client. To be your own psychologist may seem to smack of the same principle, but unless your tension is of such a psychotic degree that you need psychiatric help, when you read with an open mind and apply the simple remedies herein presented, I know that they can be of help.

Most people think that relaxation is the cure for tension. This is not quite true, for if relaxation means to stop work and to do something restful or enjoyable, in essence all it does is provide temporary escape from the essential problems that are making you tense. When your golf game or Caribbean vacation is over, you will be just as tense as you were before you took the plane or the golf cart.

If you suffer with these tension problems, you and only

you know what it really is that is making you tense. Only you know why you are becoming a nervous wreck. It may be some minor problem such as overweight or strained personal relations at work or with a member of your family, problems that to an outsider seem trivial or ridiculous. But this central problem is not trivial to you. It has assumed the proportions of a Frankenstein monster that is so threatening in your mind that it is making you miserable. And tension is misery. In some it can be agonizing. The purpose of this book is to tell you what you can do about it.

The first thing you must do requires more courage than you think you possess, but it is the essential first step and one that you have not yet taken. You know that you are in a constant state of nerves. You know that you are tense and unhappy, and you know *why* you are in this miserable condition. But, do you have the simple intestinal fortitude—do you have the guts—to bring your probem out of the closet of your mind and examine it in the clear sunshine of reality? Do you constantly brush the problem under a mental rug? Could it be that you are afraid to face up to the cause of your tension, and rather than make the conscious act of will required to face up to your problem, you prefer to suffer the continuous pain of nervous tension? If so, stop passing the buck! Stop being dishonest with yourself! Stop being a mental coward, and you will stop being a tense, emotional wreck.

Right now, right this minute, take the first step. It is easier than you think, and no matter how weak you think you may be, you can do it. You *must* do it. Face up to it and ask yourself the question to which only you have the answer: What is it that is making me tense? Think about it honestly. Write it down on a piece of paper. Admit the truth to yourself and you will have begun your own therapy. Don't be ashamed. You do not have to tell anyone else, but if you know and admit the primary cause of your tension, you have taken the first step toward its elimination.

I do not know what your problem may be. I do not really care. You know, and that is all that matters. Now that you have discovered or admitted what it is, try to decide logically and realistically what you can do about it. Maybe you feel inadequate in your home, in your work, or in your life. Admit it. Jack is a better salesman, or Mary is a better secretary. Maybe the wives of your husband's friends are more glamorous or more intelligent or have better figures than you do. It is almost certain that you can do something about it. But even if you can't, the worst thing you can do is not admit your central problem and escape into the guilt of self-pity, which is an essential ingredient of tension and unhappiness.

Your tension may come from any one of a thousand causes. A feeling of inadequacy is only one. In your specific case it may be the simple one of overwork—that you are driving yourself too hard. Think about it. Then do something about it. Give up that extra part-time job even if you cannot buy that new car or dishwasher. Maybe you are not working hard enough. You know if you are basically lazy and your tension is compounded of a feeling of guilt. Try to change. Force yourself. Until you try, really try, you will be unable even to nibble away at your tension.

Tension is a habit, just as success is a habit—and failure. Break the mental habit that is making you tense and you will break the tension itself. You may think,

"That's easy enough to say but how can I do it?" More likely you will say, "He doesn't understand." It doesn't matter whether I understand or your family understands. What matters is that you understand.

You have now made your first effort—to understand the reason for your tension. Happily, in most cases, if you are honest with yourself, you have made the first move to eliminate it. There are cases, and yours may be one of them, where there is no logical reason for tension. If you honestly believe that there is no reason for yours, we will go on to some relaxation techniques I will outline to ameliorate your tense condition.

But first be honest. Have you really found the primary cause of your tension? Have you resolved to do something about it? Only if you have honestly faced up to what is eating you should you proceed with the two-pronged attack against the tension dragon. The other half of your pincer attack is relaxation.

RELAXATION

The word "relax" means different things to different people. To some it means to cease work, to play, rest, vacation, or exercise. To others it means to ignore reality, to avoid responsibility, to hide from problems rather than face them. Most of us want a relaxed life. Few know how to accomplish it. When people hear the title of this book, many say, "I need that—I wish I could relax."

Recently, when I told a friend how busy I've been the last few years with my writing, he said, "Why don't you take some of your own medicine? You're retired. Why don't you relax?" By his simple statement my friend told me three things: He didn't enjoy his work; he lacked a clear idea of what true relaxation means; and he is one of millions of Americans who need help in learning relaxation techniques. To him, work and tension were synonymous. Actually, keeping busy is one of life's surest roads to relaxation—if your industry is properly directed and controlled. The truth is that I am more relaxed when busy writing and sharing than while idle. In fact, sharing is one of the basic secrets of the truly relaxed life.

Relaxation does not mean idleness, irresponsibility, a lack of interest or concern. Nor does it mean a refusal to face facts. It does not mean looking only at the favorable side or ignoring a problem in the hope that the problem will somehow disappear. Nor does a change of activity necessarily assure a relaxed mental attitude. Going fishing, golfing, skiing, attending a show or sports event should be an enjoyable and relaxing diversion. But unless the tense and harried individual leaves irksome problems behind when he closes the shop or office door, he will derive little benefit from the change from labor to recreation.

No use pretending—fighting problems subconsciously, whether at work or play, only makes the victim more tense and jittery. You can pretend to yourself and others all you will—you seldom fool one and never fool the other. Deep within, each individual knows when he is trying to f wl himself. Relaxing with a false self is far more difficult than honestly facing up to any problem. Integrity and self-respect demand that a man first be true to himself.

Realism is of primary importance. To be truly relaxed

an individual must learn to live a well-balanced life. He must be mature. He must live a well-adjusted, rational existence—one that is physically, mentally, and spiritually harmonious. And this must be without regard to problems, responsibilities, environment, or neurotic neighbors. The relaxed person seeks to change what can and should be changed. He accepts the unchangeable with as much good grace and understanding as is humanly possible.

If you would live a relaxed life, you must be your own doctor. You will be only as tension tossed as you allow yourself to be. And you will be as relaxed as you make up your mind to be—and no more. To relax, or not to relax, is your own decision. Remember as you read the remaining chapters that the choice is up to you.

To relax means first of all to be realistic—to cool it, to simmer down, to roll with the punches, to face life as it is, not as we'd like it to be. That is the secret and the true meaning of relaxation. And that is what this book is all about.

WHY DON'T WE RELAX?

Modern life is subject to so many pressures, demands, fears, and frustrations that man is prone to become tense, jumpy, and distraught. Many of us are overworked, overorganized and overwhelmed. We punish ourselves with too much activity in the midst of noise and confusion. We allow ourselves too little free time, rest, and quietude. We undertake too much—attend too many functions, have too many appointments, serve on too many committees, belong to too many organizations. Between our drives, distractions, and duties, we dash about madly in all directions. Under pressure from one strain and crisis after another, when finally free at close of day we often find ourselves too empty, hollow, and fatigued to rest and relax.

Modern man is constantly beset with problems. Being human, we too often allow negative factors to make us depressed or even bitter. Tension is the inevitable result. Under physical, mental, and emotional stresses, we tend to react like uncivilized barbarians. Ours is not the ideal environment for relaxing. Yet it is our world, and man must adjust realistically to conditions as he finds them.

When a sensible person has a cold, or headache, or a pain, he dashes for the medicine chest, or the doctor. Why don't we use the same good judgment when we get jittery, nervous, and tense? Why don't we do something about it before it gets worse? Why let these negative factors continue until they become a pattern? Left unchecked, negative traits and tendencies soon become wrong fixed habits, and fixed habits are not easily broken.

Why don't people relax? Some don't know how. Some know how, but don't even try. Many are too apathetic. Many are too conformity-conscious; they fear public opinion. Many haven't learned to discipline themselves.

"People are so much like people" that they often fail to see and do the obvious. Many just can't bring themselves to do the simple things they know they ought to do. So they let their problems ride on their shoulders and minds until they are so bowed down they lose perspective—and they become tense.

WHO NEEDS IT?

The inability to relax, frequently rationalized as normal nervousness, generally results from needless tension. Left uncorrected too long, it leads to emotional instability.

Fear, frustration, tension, and worry cause more loss of manpower and economic production—and more unhappiness—than all of man's organic and physical ills, plus all the casualties of war. The need to relax is everywhere apparent. If you feel the need, but can't, don't despair. You are no oddball. You have lots of company—and you can learn.

Tension is no respecter of place or person. It is just as likely to be present in a clerk as in the company president. Women are as likely victims as men. Even children suffer from tension. Young or old, rich or poor, busy or idle, no segment of society is exempt. The ravages of emotional disharmonies in our society are everywhere apparent. People who cannot learn to live with the harsh realities of modern life suffer nervous days and sleepless nights.

Man's crying need to relax demands less emotional hysteria and more self-control and spiritual stamina. The following statistics indicate something of the need for wider knowledge and practice of the art of relaxation.

According to one survey, 90 percent of all the people who fail in life do so not because of any lack of ability to succeed, but because they quit too soon. They lack the will, the courage, the faith, the mental or moral stamina —whatever it is—to win. Feeling inadequate, they become discouraged just when an extra lunge might take them over the hump. So it is with many tense, jumpy people. They are no different from their relaxed neighbors—except that they tend to fold and quit in confusion just when an additional spurt of optimism is essential.

A survey of 100 large corporations indicated that 85 percent of all the persons separated from their places of employment were not discharged for any lack of technical ability or education or know-how. They were released because of their inability to get along with other people. This allergy to people made them so standoffish, tense, and uncongenial that they were undesirable as employees.

One federal personnel officer estimates that 55 percent of the many civil service employees forced into early retirement on physical disability benefits have no known organic physical impairment. "They are," he states, "on the physical disability rolls because of emotional instability. They live under tension instead of in a relaxed atmosphere."

Dr. E. Stanley Jones says, "It is the consensus of medical opinion that forty to sixty percent of all our diseases are rooted in wrong attitudes of mind and spirit." The American Medical Association puts it at 50 percent—only one-half of man's ills are physical in origin; the other half are rooted in mental and spiritual weakness.

Apparently the ratio is growing. One medical doctor believes that 85 percent of his patients need no physician. He says, "They need to change their mental and spiritual attitudes. These people are passing on the sickness of their minds and souls to their bodies."

According to reliable statistics, one out of every two beds in all the hospitals in the United States is occupied by a person who either is confined by a nervous disorder or who suffers a physical illness induced by an emotional upset.

In 1955 it was estimated that poor, frightened, distressed souls went insane at the appalling rate of one every two and one-half minutes of every day. And each year the casualty list has continued to increase.

Many Americans commit suicide each year. In their abject confusion, out of a sense of hopelessness and despair, these unfortunate people decide they can no longer live with themselves.

Constant contact with persons and things tends to rub us the wrong way, causing friction and nervous tension. We must learn to insulate ourselves against these high-tension wires or we will be burned up inside. No doubt, tension maims and kills millions each year. Tension destroys homes and happiness and people. Tension makes people old and old-looking before their time.

Who needs to relax? Almost every human being on the face of the earth. Some know how, but many do not. For the latter group this book offers a ray of hope.

WHAT'S IN IT FOR ME?

What can you gain by becoming a relaxed person? Why should you want to relax? There are practical reasons. Here are ten of the more obvious ones:

1. If you are relaxed, *you will be healthier*. Tension and ill health travel together. Allow yourself to get too tense too often and you can make yourself ill. Tension is a disease of the mind that quickly transmits itself to other parts of the body. Tension feeds upon itself as it poisons and contaminates everything and everyone it touches.

2. *You will be more popular*. A relaxed person wears

better socially. When you are calm and relaxed, others are at ease. People like to be with those in whose presence they feel comfortable.

3. *You will make more friends.* If you want a test, try this. Take time in a roomful of strangers to make some ill-at-ease person feel at home. He'll relax and so will you. And you will make a friend for life.

4. *You will be more successful.* You will work better. You will be a better leader. You will be more polished, poised, and capable. You will have more self-confidence and you will merit the confidence of others. You will increase your ability to get things done and you will inspire others to greater accomplishment.

5. *You will develop a better personality.* Nothing in this world is so upsetting as a human being out of control. Tension, fear, animosity, frustration, and worry can convert an otherwise pleasing personality into a pathetic inhuman being.

6. *You will be better looking.* Bitterness and tension show in your face. Failure to relax is soon followed by a drawn face, a shifty eye, and a sullen expression. Tension can make a good face ugly and unattractive. If you have peace in your mind and heart it will be reflected in your face.

7. *You will become a better speaker.* The abject terror of a frightened speaker can make an otherwise educated person look and sound like an idiot. When a speaker is tense and ill at ease, he makes his listeners nervous and uncomfortable too. You will do your audience and yourself a great kindness if you can stand before them relaxed.

8. *You will sleep better at night.* No one can enjoy a restful sleep as long as he carries a load on his mind at

night. The relaxed person learns to lay aside his problems as he drops his last shoe.

9. *You will be happier.* You will get much more fun out of life if you can adjust and accept with good grace what cannot be changed. The prime purpose of this book is to help you roll with the punches and count your blessings instead of counting and recounting your problems.

10. *You will live longer* if you take time to really live. Take the time and make the effort to relax. Your life will be greatly enriched through the years.

HOW CAN I RELAX?

If by relaxing we mean remaining calm and collected no matter what the sudden crisis, we are hoping for perfection. Man is constantly at war with his environment. That is inevitable. But he need not be constantly at war with himself. To really relax, an individual must be calm without and within. When man is at peace with himself, his neighbor, and his Maker, he relaxes automatically.

Most of us are prone to put off living until tomorrow—until we've made our fortune or until we retire. Instead of relaxing, we grow more problem conscious and confused. We spin our wheels. We rev up our mental and emotional engine and burn it without going anywhere.

To relax, you must be aware of the pitfalls and dangers of emotional and physical hysteria. You must learn to recognize and put an end to tension producers. You can if you really try. Once you pass from a constant state of tension to the complete absence of tension in your life, you will have mastered the art of relaxation. It is up to you. Our tensions come from something we are doing or not doing. They are usually the result of physical or emotional strain. Remove that strain and you will relax. Tension is the sand in life's machinery. Remove that sand and your whole personality will become lubricated and relaxed.

It is physically impossible to be both tense and relaxed at the same time. Tension keeps you off balance, unnatural and uncomfortable. Take off the pressure and your nerve muscles will gradually return to normal. So —"untense." Let go. Let down your hair. Unlimber and unwind. Simmer down. Stop rushing and fretting over trifles. Take it slow and easy—one step at a time. Be calm and collected. Relax—without and within.

Don't allow yourself to give way to spasms of nerves. Be sensible. Keep physically and mentally fit. Do all those seemingly simple little things you know you ought to do —but don't. This approach may seem too easy—too trite and uncomplicated. But it is the only practical, realistic solution.

Use your God-given talents and good judgment to guide your emotional behavior as well as your physical activities. Do your best—then rest secure in the knowledge that no one who has done his best has any cause to worry or be apprehensive. Live one day at a time.

Above all else, don't invite failure by negative thinking. Think positively. By your attitude you make your own luck, good or bad. Expect and deserve to win, but be prepared to lose. Be ready for shocks, reverses, and disappointments. But always expect and deserve to win.

If your tensions are to be kept under control, pettiness

must be put aside. Irritations, animosities, prejudices, hatreds, and jealousies only add to problems. Turmoil, problems, and dark clouds all have a way of passing. Often the bitter pill produces lasting results long after the unpleasant taste is forgotten.

If you earnestly seek to lead a more relaxed life, you can. It is strictly up to you. Only you can determine how serene your life shall be. One relaxed old-timer, about to retire, was asked how he kept his pleasant disposition. "By avoiding unnecessary pressure," he replied. "Years ago I decided to set my alarm clock fifteen minutes earlier and enjoy taking my time. It worked so well I've been doing it ever since." There are many similar little things you can do to avoid pressure before it gets started. To truly relax, you must learn to cultivate your own garden of quietude, tranquillity, and inner peace. These constitute the relaxed spirit.

Don't just think and talk and read about relaxation. Do something about it. As you read, check the parts of this book that apply to you. Then reread and rethink and relax as you put these pertinent parts to work in your life.

There are no instant or miraculous solutions to all of life's problems. But many rational answers are to be found in simple approaches. This book is a composite of such wisdom, gleaned from specialists in their respective fields. And many, like the writer, have through personal experience earned some right to speak. Furthermore, this book seeks to encourage greater participation, because the approach to relaxation is simple, practical, and enjoyable. It is only through a proper attitude and a realistic approach to life that relaxation can be achieved. As you learn to relax with the help of this book, you will enjoy a pleasant experience. It's easy to do. You will find you have acquired the relaxing habit as you learn to unbend, unwind, and live as a normal human being should: unafraid, unhurried, and untense. This is a do-it-yourself book. The whole man is under consideration. Too many writers have concerned themselves with symptoms only. This book's approach seeks to help you locate and control tensions in all areas—physical, mental, and spiritual—both before and after they start. This book can be worth its weight in gold—if you apply its simple truths. It can help you to help yourself relax. I dare you to really try it.

2

Eliminate
Physical Tension

Are you nervous, tense, irritable, and depressed? Do you suffer with tension headaches? Are you prone to lash out in bitterness and anger at friend and foe alike, with or without cause? Do you have that tired, worn-out, letdown feeling constantly? Are you listless and sluggish, sometimes dizzy? Such symptoms may result from tension, but more likely it's simply your digestive system backfiring.

If you are subject to periodic headaches, don't worry about it too much. It's nothing to get tense about. You're probably normal. A headache is not necessarily all bad. It is your inbuilt, automatic warning signal that tells you when something goes wrong with your system. If heeded promptly and properly, your headache can serve a very useful purpose. The most frequent causes of a normal headache are an upset stomach, too much eyestrain, too little oxygen, or unusual excitement. Your headache could come from fatigue; a physical blow or shock; bad teeth; ear, nose, or throat trouble; or numerous minor causes. If left uncorrected, a chronic slight headache can trigger a chronic neurosis that can cause you some real headaches.

Aspirin, or any one of a dozen pills or drugs, may be used to give relief. But don't become a pill addict. You may be putting your warning signal system to sleep. Your headache could be a symptom of something far more serious. If the trouble persists, don't just suffer and worry and become tense. Consult your doctor.

Persistent headaches always cause tension. And the tensions that come from mental strain, nerves, and the pressure of problems can result in tension headaches. If your trouble stems from physical causes, put yourself in your doctor's hands. But if yours is really a tension headache, you may find this chapter exceedingly helpful. Read it carefully, and relax.

Tension headache is more mental than physical. It can result from the overstrained nerves and muscles of people who have lost perspective. But almost always tension headaches result from wrong thinking, negative attitudes, or emotional excesses. Tension is little more than high-strung, taut nerves. Like wire springs kept too long under pressure, you nerves will snap and break. Overstrained nerves or muscles are much like the clenched jaw, the closed fist, or the closed mind that won't pry open. Left unchecked, tension impairs your effectiveness. It can cause nervous breakdown or eventually impair or even destroy your health.

Tension, trouble, and turmoil are the lot of man. But why allow yourself to crack up over what cannot be helped? Mankind has always lived in a hectic atmosphere. The very existence of our forefathers depended upon back-breaking work in a hazardous environment. Life was in constant jeopardy in those early days. And primitive man suffered even greater hazards, yet survived. He was too busy in the fight for survival to let himself grow tense over trivialities. Why should any intelligent human being become overconcerned with what he will eat, or drink, or wear? Basic needs are increasingly available today, even to those allergic to labor. And if recent fashion trends continue, man's clothing needs will become minimal, to put it mildly.

Tension is sometimes said to be frowning all over. If a facial frown requires sixty-four muscles, just imagine the nerve and muscle strain when the whole body gets tense. Tension causes people to do strange things. Some years ago the chairman of an important banquet in the Washington D.C., Statler Hotel got so nervous and tense over the delayed arrival of the honored guest that he fainted dead away and had to be held upright on his chair while someone else greeted the guest. One man who stuttered from childhood appeared to be incurable, although doctors could find no organic impairment. A friend, suspecting that tension might be responsible, encouraged him to enroll in a speech course. He conquered his fear, eliminated his tension, and overcame his stuttering, all within four short months.

All tensions, whether mental or physical, are artificially created. All of us are subjected to pressures of some kind

—physical, emotional, or economic. It is sometimes difficult to keep our mental and emotional equilibrium in this topsy-turvy world, but man is still his own greatest problem.

Emotional tensions are caused by fears and frustrations; by anxiety, pessimism, prejudice, hatred, animosity, and all our secret irritations. We travel at too fast a pace. We indulge in too many excesses. We are so overstimulated and so underrelaxed that frequently we develop a neuromuscular condition known as nervous hypertension. Symptoms of the disease are easily recognized. The victim usually is jumpy, jerky, impatient, and constantly in a whirl. He suffers intense headaches, with batting of the eyes, biting of the nails, and labored breathing. He may smoke excessively, is easily depressed, perspires freely even on cold days, and feels alternately hot and cold inside and out. He sighs often, panics easily, and is emotionally unstable.

In its advanced stages, hypertension can cause peptic ulcers, skin disorders, and even malfunctioning of the sex organs. If allowed to run rampant, tension can cause high blood pressure, palpitation of the heart, hypertensive angina, or even bring on a coronary thrombosis. And a full-blown physiological and psychological neurosis often is responsible for persistent insomnia, insanity, and even suicide.

Although it starts as a simple emotional upheaval, nervous hypertension is no imaginary ailment. It can become a very real and serious condition which requires expert help. And fortunately there is today a profusion of professional help—much of it good. But all the medical doctors, psychiatrists, psychologists, and physiotherapists in the world cannot cure your tension, unless you first help yourself.

How do you help yourself? There is a specific law of physiology that states that "one cannot be excited and relaxed at the same time." So don't overdo it. Don't flip your emotional lid. Slow down. Take it easy. Relax. And remember, relaxation is a do-it-yourself art.

Experts tell us that to avoid fatigue we should rest before we get tired. "Never stand when you can sit. And never sit if you can lie down." One old-timer had the right idea. Asked the secret of his longevity, he replied, "I take it easy. When I work, I work easy. When I sit, I sit loose. And when I rest, I fall asleep." A better formula for relaxation was never devised.

Relaxation has a therapeutic effect on your body and your mind. Its benefits as a prophylactic and curative agent are conclusive. Under therapeutic relaxation, the individual comes to feel a serene sense of well-being. He ceases to be apprehensive. He stops worrying. He starts acting like a rational human being and lives a rational emotional life.

The real secret of overcoming tension is to rule it out before it rules you. Nip it in the bud. But how can you really know the tension danger signal? The beekeeper said to his new assistant, "If the bees crowd you too much, back off slowly, and remember, don't run unless necessary." "How will I know when it's necessary?" the new recruit wanted to know. "Don't worry," said the bee-keeper, "when the time comes, you'll know."

Tension comes in progressive, recognizable stages. It starts with vague nervousness. As it increases in intensity, your voice gets shrill and high pitched. You become jittery, irritable, hot, flushed; you perspire freely and almost always have a headache. Shortness of breath, sharp pains in the chest, and numbness in the left upper arm soon follow. By now the bees have you well on the run. Advanced hypertension brings on insomnia, heart trouble, ulcers, hallucinations, and tense associates.

If you can just make up your mind right now to do these three simple things, you will head off serious tension.

1. Never undertake more work, appointments, or assignments than you can carry calmly, quietly, and without hurry, flurry, and worry.

2. Never devote more time or concern to any one problem than it merits. Make decisions promptly and never second-guess yourself once a decision is made. And never, never brood or worry over what can't be helped.

3. The instant you feel yourself becoming unduly nervous or upset, stop, look, and listen. Stop. Don't just pause—stop short. And remain still until good sense prevails. Take a good look at the situation. Talk it over with yourself. Say to yourself, "Hold it, old buddy, this kind of thing is silly. Stop it right now." Think, if necessary meditate and pray until serenity and composure return.

"But," you may say, "as children we were told that only crazy people talk to themselves." Nothing could be farther from the facts, so don't be misled by such nonsense. It is good psychology to reason and argue things out audibly and listen to yourself. You'll find it most effective. That is why the better sales courses employ this technique in their training programs so effectively. Besides, you are the only person in the world who can call you a fool to your face with impunity. You are the only one to whom you'll listen under such circumstances. And who is better qualified to give a realistic appraisal? So talk it over with yourself reasonably and rationally.

A very successful contractor and builder of state roads and bridges frequently employed this technique, although I'm not quite sure that he knew it. When confronted with a tricky problem, he'd ask first one, then another, of his small crew of workmen. "What would you do about this?" I doubt that he ever accepted or even heard their suggestions. Usually he'd cut them short with, "No, that wouldn't work, here's what I think I'll do." Then he'd outline his plan, which, incidentally, he didn't always follow after he had talked it over some more with himself. To his workers the contractor may have seemed contrary and peculiar. But the truth is that the contractor was reasoning out the proposed approach as he talked. This is perhaps why he made so much money building small bridges, culverts, and tricky problem jobs that most contractors dreaded. He made his mistakes in conversation, before he started using expensive labor, concrete, and steel. Don't hesitate to talk it over with yourself. If you get caught, you can always fall back on the absent-minded-professor gambit.

Try the Carnegie problem-solving technique. Ask yourself, "What is the problem?" Then write down the answer. Ask, "What can I do to correct it?" Then list all the possible solutions. Select the most logical approach, start at once to put it into effect, and don't look back. Do it, if you can. And if you can't, then try the next best. Meanwhile, keep encouraging yourself. Repeat aloud this portion of the 118th Psalm: "The Lord is on my side; I will not fear. . . . This is the day which the Lord hath made. . . . Let us rejoice and be glad in it."

LIVE WITH YOUR NERVES

If you awaken some morning to discover that you have nerves and are jumpy and nervous, don't worry too much about it. Everyone does. Like sex, your nerves are here to stay. You may as well learn to live with them.

Remember that your nerves are a valuable, normal, and necessary part of your personality. Nervousness is the difference between a high-strung racehorse, champing at the bit, and a cow that is docile, listless, and content to stand around chewing her cud. There is a world of difference between normal nervousness and self-destructive tension. Why not accept and use your nerves to drive you on to greater accomplishment? Your nervous system is one of the most vital segments of your anatomy. Learn to live with it rationally.

The human body is not mere flesh and blood and bone. This complex mechanism we call the human body comprises a series of distinct systems. These include the skeletal, the nervous, the organic, the alimentary, the respiratory, and the circulatory. Each of these systems, including the nervous system, must work in perfect harmony with all the others, or imbalance and sickness result.

Your body is the most complex system of intricate, interrelated parts operating a single functional unit ever devised. It is far more complicated than a spaceship. Despite centuries of accumulated and classified knowledge in the medical profession many of its mysteries remain unsolved. Perhaps that is why we still say that doctors are "practicing medicine."

Your nervous system is the control center of all your

activities. It is the control tower or alert station that records sensations good and bad, warns of danger, relays signals from brain to muscle, and returns physical sensation. When the brain's control tower signals anxiety or danger, your nerves warn you to prepare for flight or stand and fight. If it is fight, you'll probably win. If it is flight, you will likely lose.

Under overstress, nerves strain and get as tight as a taut rubber band. Under prolonged and unbearable tension a neurosis develops and the band snaps. This is called a malfunction of the nervous system. As in a space launch a malfunction can mean disaster. The real purpose of your nerves and your nervous system is to regulate and control the rational action of a healthy body.

So don't write your nerves off as something bad or undesirable. Learn to understand and live with them. Be thankful that you have a nervous system. Don't abuse it—use it.

Speech and nerves come into conflict if we keep our feelings bottled up. Communication is the link that unites us with our fellowmen. Our thoughts, our feelings, will not forever bear being unexpressed. The best tension relievers are the spillways built into the structure of our lives that carry the constant flow of our thoughts and feelings into the world around us. In a desperate world, we need communication to understand the strangers we constantly confront. But because of nerves, man often hesitates to communicate with his neighbor.

The human brain has been facetiously described as "that astounding mechanism that starts to function at birth and doesn't stop until its owner is first called upon to speak in public." In my seventeen years as head of the Washington branch of the Dale Carnegie School, I learned that nervous speech jitters are no respecters of persons. They attack giants of industry, professional men and women, farmers, and clerks. Most persons, regardless of age, sex, or status, react alike until they become adjusted, with nerves under control.

A Marine hero of Guadalcanal said, "I was more nervous on the platform than I was in the hottest of the enemy flack." Yet that man, Joe Foss, conquered his fear, trained himself to be an effective speaker, and became governor of the state of South Dakota.

A wealthy executive once told Dale Carnegie this interesting story: "During the war I was asked to appear in Boston to receive a government award won by one of my corporations. The very idea of being called upon to respond at a public gathering literally made me ill. I was panic-stricken. I first made sure that the time and date were firmly set and couldn't well be changed, then I said, 'I'm sorry, I've just checked my schedule and I'm due in Cleveland for an important business meeting on that date. I'll arrange for a junior executive to accept the award.' I was so ashamed of my cowardice that I actually rode a train all the way to Cleveland and attended an unnecessary meeting just to make good on the lies I had told. En route, I decided to join your next speech class in New York, if my identity could be kept secret." That man enrolled as Charles Brown and became an outstanding speaker. He was later appointed United States ambassador to Norway under his real name, Charles Ulrich Beh.

In seventeen years of operating a speech institute in the nation's capital, I encountered numerous cases of nervous speech jitters. Unreasoning fear and paralyzing nervous tension cause otherwise mature, rational adults to indulge in some rather strange behavior.

At the Statler Hotel in Washington, D.C., a male student suddenly disappeared from class just before he was due to make his maiden speech. Petrified with fear, the poor chap was finally located by a woman classmate who found him pacing back and forth in the ladies' powder room as he frantically puffed a cigarette. He was so unreasonably nervous that he didn't know where he was. A government official in another class had worked himself up into such a nervous frenzy in anticipation of his first speech that, when his name was finally called, he lost control of his bladder and had to be excused.

One successful executive told his class that he was taking the course in self-defense. He said, "I had been elected president of my club. When the members clamored for an acceptance speech, I was petrified. I arose reluctantly to my feet, then everything went black. I stood up but my brains remained seated. Here's what they tell me I blurted out—'Fellows, you and I both know I don't appreciate this honor, but I want to tell you I sincerely deserve it from the bottom of my heart.'"

Many people grow nervous as they travel an unknown path. But once you overcome your nervous fear in any specific area, you are well on the road to conquering all your apprehensions. Emerson said, "Do the thing you fear and the death of fear is certain." Dr. E. Stanley Jones assures us that "you lose fifty percent of your fear and nervousness the moment you acknowledge its presence and decide to do something about it." And "you lose another forty percent the instant you start to act." This indicates that 90 percent of the cause of fear and nervousness can be dissipated simply by your decision and action. If you are unduly nervous about anything, first get this 90 percent behind you. When you face the problem, then decide and act at once, and the remaining 10 percent will be easy. Soon you'll conquer and control your nerves.

Keeping your emotional equilibrium isn't easy. But it is vitally important. Don't allow yourself to become tense and fearful. Have faith. Follow the precept of Mohammad: "Trust in God, but tie your camel." Can you afford to do less? If we do our best during the day, tie our camel when we lie down at night, and trust in God, our nerves will operate to bless us. In the words of Benjamin Disraeli: "Nothing in life is more remarkable than the unnecessary anxiety which we endure." We need to understand that nerves are a natural and normal part of the anatomy, but that an upset nervous system can ruin any life. Once we adopt the right attitude and gain an understanding of our nervous system, we are more likely to accept and appreciate our nerves. With greater acceptance and appreciation, we will find it easier to live with and use our nerves to help us relax, instead of misusing them as uninsulated high-tension cables to short-circuit our emotional stability.

PHYSICAL TENSION

Tension is like the weather. Everybody talks about it, but nobody does anything about it. But unlike the weather, tension isn't inevitable. You can control or even prevent tension and be more relaxed. But only if you try, only if you work at it. You can relax in direct ratio to how well you eliminate or control your tension tendencies, both physical and mental.

Not all tensions are emotionally induced. Nor do all tensions spring from muscular excesses or strain. Either physical or mental strain can throw you. So it isn't really too important whether yours started with wrong thinking or wrong doing. Since tension begets tension, if you don't check them, your physical and mental tensions will merge into one big headache, with disastrous results for you.

An executive with too many responsibilities and an overloaded schedule found that through confusion and haste he did nothing well, got tense, and went around in circles. He had spread himself too thin. Now when he has too many things to do, instead of speeding up to try to fulfill his demanding schedule, he slows down, or stops outright. He has found that if he sits quietly for an hour and relaxes, he can start out fresh and actually accomplish much more. His relaxation break is also a tension break—and a brake on his speeding tenseness. Was this man's problem physical or mental? Probably a little of each. But, with the right solution, what's the difference? The important thing to remember is that it is infinitely better to prevent tension at its inception than to try to put out the fire after it gets you all burned up.

Overstrain of nerves and muscles for prolonged periods will cause any individual to become so tense and out of harmony with his environment that it is impossible for him to relax. Unless he learns to recognize the symptoms and to master the technique of muscular relaxation, he can soon become a victim of chronic muscular hypertension.

Wrong body postures, with muscles under contraction,

inevitably cause taut, tense muscles. The best antidote to such tenseness is proper exercise. Proper physical exercise at the right time probably would have avoided such tension in the first place. As you relax the voluntary muscles over which you have control, your internal muscles and organs over which you have little or no direct control will also relax. As you master the technique of muscular relaxation, mental strains will lessen, and gradually internal, organic tenseness will also tend to decrease.

Excessive or unnatural nerve and muscle activity can be corrected by what the professional physiotherapist calls "progressive relaxation." By this phrase he means cultivated, natural physical relaxation, step by step, until relaxation becomes automatic and habitual. No attempt is made here to teach scientific relaxation. Physiological relaxation through muscular therapy is a highly developed science. Supervised training, under the guidance of a competent physiotherapist, should be sought if, and when, needed. Numerous books on muscular therapy and progressive relaxation by qualified experts are available. Or, if you feel the need for physical fitness exercise, consult your doctor or any gym or health club counselor.

A word of caution about muscular therapy and exercising merely for exercise's sake. Don't overdo it. Too much exercise can be just as harmful as too little. One tension-tossed, middle-aged bachelor was determined not to get bored when he retired from his federal government job. He later bragged that he kept active every hour of the day. And he did, for a time. Each weekday morning he played three or four sets of tennis. Each afternoon he teed off for eighteen holes of golf, then really teed off on the nineteenth. Saturday night he danced until long after midnight. A salesman friend kept a similar inhuman pace. Both exhausted men were quietly laid to rest before reaching sixty-five.

Moderation in all things is as good a guideline for living today as it was two thousand years ago in ancient Rome. Eight hours for labor, eight hours for mental and physical refreshment, and eight hours for rest is still a practical formula, though not practiced enough. Your body, like your mind, needs leisure, recreation, and rest, as well as work.

Take time for reasonable relaxation. Take a short vacation as often as practicable. To get away, if only momentarily, from chores and problems is in itself of unquestioned therapeutic value.

For the average person relaxation simply means recreation. It means golfing, fishing, swimming, or skiing. It means going to a baseball or football game, to the races, to the mountains, or to the seashore. As long as it is a vacation away from work, it's called relaxation. But this isn't necessarily true. Too many people remain tense even during leisure periods. For many recreation becomes merely an escape hatch from business and other problems, which they carry with them subconsciously. An attorney recently confided that because he had carried his tensions with him on a particular day, his golf game was off. Through anxiety and impatience he failed to concentrate on his next shot. The moral is clear—take life one step at a time.

Vexing problems are to be expected in the normal course of any line of work. These need not throw you if you have the proper attitude toward your occupation and toward life in general. Having work to do—a job that must be done and that needs you to do it—is occupational therapy at its best. Work becomes play, and the solving of problems a game to the right man in the right job. Unless you like your job, change it. Change it today, for you've already waited too long. Don't fight it and kill yourself with tension. Get with it, or get away from it before it gets you down. Life is too short not to get enjoyment out of everything you do. Get a little fun out of life as you go through. Especially at your job, where you spend the greatest portion of your active hours.

Frequently it is physical rather than mental tensions that are the direct cause of much of our failure to relax. Many of these are the result of inexcusable thoughtlessness. In the office, store, or plant, too often we sit, stand or work in awkward, muscle-straining positions unnecessarily.

Occupational therapy has long been an important science. Much has been learned about "differential relaxation" and "residual tension." Differential relaxation is a high-sounding phrase that means relaxing during an activity. Simply stated, it means using the minimum muscle required, with the least possible tension and strain, meanwhile relaxing all the other muscles.

Large corporations pay high-priced efficiency experts and industrial engineers to streamline work operations and conditions. These experts help the employee accomplish his task with a minimum of effort and strain, saving millions in man-hours and money through greater productivity.

Don't crouch or stoop when you can stand upright, these experts caution. Don't stand on one foot when you can use two more comfortably. Don't remain too long in one position. Change your body position before fatigue sets in, not after.

Vary your operation when possible, rather than continuing the same grind all day. Change your stance, make your job work with you, not against you. It all sounds very elementary. It is, but production increases have proved that these expensive experts are a profitable investment. Above all else, employees are urged not to allow themselves to get bored or tense. The efficiency experts recommend frequent coffee breaks, recesses, and rest periods. Management has learned that if an employee gets a sense of accomplishment out of his work and enjoys it, his production will increase. When your occupation becomes enjoyment instead of drudgery, you've solved both your production problem and your occupational therapy problem.

"Residual tension" is the term used to describe the tension that is left over when you have ceased all your activity. It is continued muscle contraction after exertion. It comprises the involuntary reflex actions or movements that may occur during waking hours, or even in sleep. Residual tension is indicated by jerky nerve spasms, twitching of the facial muscles, arms, or legs, by batting of the eyes, jerking of the head, or any spasmodic, involuntary movement of other parts of the body. When residual tension settles in the mind, it produces potentially even more serious problems. It can result in all kinds of nervous disorders even though no known problem exists. These are mental reactions to leftover physical strains that can set off a further disastrous chain reaction of tensions.

The best way to correct residual tension, or any tension, is to avoid overstrain before it sets in. To do this successfully, you must be tension conscious—maintain an awareness and sense of tenseness in yourself and others.

Put yourself on tension alert. Recognize the symptoms in time and you will probably be able to head off the attack. You can ward off physical tension if you will. The first rule is to keep the body muscles free from overstrain and overstress. Use your environment and the circumstances that you are contending with. Don't let them misuse you. Stay on top—don't be crushed under the load.

How? It is quite simple. Swim with the tide, not against it. If you must buck the trend, don't collide with it head on. Side step. Save your body muscles from tension and strain.

The first Henry Ford, one of the world's greatest exponents of efficiency, had the right idea. He never would allow employees to work under unnecessarily adverse conditions or without periodic rest periods.

Dale Carnegie, one of the world's greatest speakers and speech authorities, never worked or ate just prior to an important speaking engagement. He believed that most of people's dullness on and off the platform was due to fatigue, stress, or a lack of preparation, rather than lack of mentality. Before an important lecture, he always stretched out for at least an hour and, with eyes closed in complete relaxation, reviewed his forthcoming talk. As a consequence, he walked out on the platform fresh, alert, relaxed, and full of enthusiasm.

Avoid unnecessary physical tension if you wish to be more relaxed. This won't assure complete success, but it will go a long way to help you relax. It is an easy course to follow. Remember that most of your physical tensions are needless and can be avoided—if you plan it that way. Plan to avoid, rather than battle, your physical tensions. You will have taken a giant step on the road to relaxation.

MUSCULAR RELAXATION THE EASY WAY

Recognized authorities differ greatly on the subject of tension reduction and relaxation. Some would only treat the mind. Some would have us deal primarily with nerves. But most authorities agree that to be relaxed you first must get your muscles to relax. Certainly it must be obvious that relaxation at its best involves the whole man—body, mind, and spirit. Their relative importance may be debatable and may vary from case to case, but there can be no doubt that the whole man is vitally involved. The greatest fallacy of this sophisticated age is the unrealistic attempts by many so-called experts to compartmentalize human personality.

No personality is all body, all mind, or all spirit. When frustrating tensions prevail, the individual is tense all over. When peace, calm, and serenity reign, the whole man is free of tension and therefore completely relaxed. Medical authorities cannot even agree upon which physical area is first in importance. Different experts point out three different high-tension areas. Conquer this or that area, says each group, and you'll conquer your tensions.

Some experts believe the eyes to be the key. Many are equally sure it is the vocal area. Still others insist that the real seat of tension is the heart. All are agreed that the eye, the larynx, and the heart are certainly three key muscles. And most medical authorities are in agreement that, if these three high-tension areas are devoid of tension at any one time, then you are most likely to simmer down and relax physically.

This may explain why doctors, psychiatrists, and other

counselors recommend that the patient lie down periodically for a fifteen-minute nap to relax and rest. There is
no better medicine to restore frayed nerves than natural
sleep and rest. Stretching out or sitting quietly for brief
rest periods of as little as three minutes will help you
relax. This is especially true if you rest with eyes closed,
lips shut, and mind as blank as you can make it. Remain
perfectly still, calm, and quiet, and your mind and body
will relax.

To this formula, the more spiritually inclined recommend the addition of meditation and prayer. Just uttering
a short prayer as you come to rest, to be thankful for your
many blessings, and to mentally exude goodwill and
blessings toward others, will soothe your spirit. And you
know something? It works. Try it. A spirit in tune with the
Infinite is utterly relaxed. No matter who, where, or what
you happen to be, meditation and prayer are good psychology, good philosophy, good religion—and good relaxation techniques.

Among authorities who hold that the eye is the most
important tension area is Dr. Edmund Jacobson of the
University of Chicago. He says, "If you can completely
relax the muscles of the eye, you can forget all your
troubles." The reason the eyes rate such importance in
relieving nervous tension, some experts maintain, is that
the eyes burn up one-fourth of all the nervous energy
consumed by the body. People with perfectly sound vision
suffer eyestrain and grow tense from prolonged reading in
bad light or other eye abuse. Under strain too long the
eyes become tense. The strained eye forgets to blink
normally and fails to perform its function of moistening
the eyeball. As a consequence strain and tension mount.

If you are reading for a long time, or driving your car

in a rainstorm, or if visibility is otherwise poor, pause periodically and exercise your eyes. Close them for thirty seconds, then open them wide and let them wander about freely for a few moments, rolling them from side to side. This will reduce the strain. Then close your eyes tight and remain quiet and still for thirty seconds. Now open and close your eyes in rapid succession, batting them until tears gather. Open your eyes wide, stare straight ahead, and let your eyeballs do the shimmy. Roll your head from side to side in a slow rotating motion, simultaneously blinking the eyes. By now your eyes should be rested and ready to serve you better.

If your eyes still feel tired and tense, perhaps you should rest from what you're doing and do something else. If that isn't possible, you might care to try a simple massage treatment behind the ears that a kind soul shared with me over fifty years ago. I still use the exercise each morning to strengthen the eye muscles. At twenty-two, I wore glasses from the time I got up in the morning until I went to bed. One day I lost my glasses in a snowstorm and for weeks was unable to visit or pay an oculist. Meanwhile I was induced to try this massage treatment, which soon strengthened my eyes so much that I didn't need glasses. Half a century later, I use glasses only when I read. Here is the exercise. Just wet the fingers well and roughly massage behind the ears as you roll your eyes in a circular motion for thirty seconds, first with eyes closed, then open. Then with eyes open use a rough towel in a behind-the-ears rubdown.

Watch out for your eyes and they will continue to watch out for you. Follow common-sense precautions to avoid eyestrain. Avoid glare, insufficient lighting, or the use of your eyes for too long a period without rest. If your work involves continuous and exacting use of your eyes under artificial or strong outside light, use an eyeshade or tinted glasses to protect your eyes from glare. Your eyes are two of the most sensitive organs of your body. Eyestrain causes tension. And tension, wherever started, eventually reflects itself in your eyes, setting off more tension, which in turn tends to magnify and increase eyestrain.

But disciples of the you-need-only-relax-the-eyes school refute their own theory. For invariably they call upon the voice and the mind and upon most of the other muscles of the body to cooperate and help the eyes perform. One authority says, "You can learn the secret of relaxing in one minute by relaxing the eye muscles." The approach he gives is a simple one, but it requires the cooperation of your mind, your will, and your voice. To relax the eye muscles we're told to "lean back, close your eyes, and say to your eyes silently, 'Let go—let go!' Say to yourself, 'Stop frowning, let go, let go!' Repeat the simple formula over and over, very slowly and deliberately, for a few minutes. Didn't you notice that after a few seconds the eyes began to obey? Didn't you feel as if some hand had wiped away the tension? You have now learned in one minute the whole secret of relaxation."

Unfortunately, this theory ignores the prominent parts played in the exercise by the mind and voice. The decision to relax started in the mind, with instructions relayed by the voice, and action carried out by the other muscles of the body. It is first a rationalization, then a doing process. First the mind, then the body must adjust and take action. Attitude of mind has more to do with absence of tension than all the subsequent physical exercise that may take place.

Just how does one let go? "Become as limp as an old

sock," or "Learn from the cat. Note how relaxed a cat is while napping. And learn to take catnaps. Watch how often your dog rests and relaxes after cavorting around, and learn from him." When we learn to relax and let go, we are at our most effective best. Often an athlete performs feats beyond his normal capabilities when he lets go all of his body tensions.

You are bound to get tense if all day long your wrong postures have been building unnatural tensions into your nerves and muscles. Wrong walking, wrong sitting, and wrong resting, for long periods, are bound to get their hold on your muscular and nervous systems, just as does wrong use of the eyes. Stop often, let go occasionally, and change your pace periodically. Correct that wrong stance now. Exercise your offended muscles and nerves until they again take their rightful place, naturally and symmetrically, in your body makeup, free of tension.

"Your voice or speech apparatus involves the most important set of muscles in the high tension area," says another school of experts. "Get your voice to relax and you will relax." It would seem that this group are telling us to keep our mouths shut. Yet they admit we use our speech apparatus, even when through the process of inner speech we say things to ourselves in a silent manner. So how can we constantly tell ourselves over and over, "Let go, do this, don't do that," yet be relaxed?

"Considerable energy is wasted in unnecessary speech," Dr. Samuel W. Gutworth points out. He says there are a "surprising number of muscles involved in the ordinary process of speaking; . . . excessive use of muscles naturally leads to fatigue," and that "excessive use of the voice muscles can cause chronic fatigue and create sufficient tension to produce mental and physical illness."

Consciously and subconsciously man talks to himself incessantly. We give ourselves pep talks, faith talks, and success talks. In every decision we make, even though no word is uttered, we give our speech muscles a workout. Some of us even talk things over in our sleep. To the lay mind it would seem that elimination of wasted effort by speech muscles would be one sure way to cultivate the art of relaxation. But normal use of these muscles is a part of healthful living. If we always speak easily and simply, in low tones, the speech therapists tell us, we will seldom suffer voice fatigue, while developing a vibrant and resonant voice. Any normal voice fatigue will be automatically overcome by adequate rest and sleep.

Properly used, your voice can be your fortune. Let tension creep in and it can become your misfortune. It is the strained, unpleasant tones and vibrations that abuse your voice and your listeners. Much of the friction in life results from the tone of the voice. Don't vocalize harsh, unpleasant thoughts through your speech apparatus. Keep a lilt in your voice and warmth in your heart and you will sidetrack many of your tension tendencies.

Calm yourself and your nerves before speaking. Don't allow yourself to get uptight inside. Tension and bitterness can be just as unkind and disastrous to your throat muscles as to any other part of your body. I had to learn this the hard way. A soft answer not only turneth away wrath, but saves you and your speech apparatus from tension wear and tear. That is why it is always vital to dominate your life with positive traits, tendencies, attitudes, and habits. When you attach yourself to something joyful and constructive, you repel the somber, gloomy side from your life and from your voice. This subject is discussed at greater length in subsequent chapters.

The heart is the vital area some experts list as the number one tension spot. It is one of man's most sensitive organs. It also is the one most abused. Heart disease kills more people in America than any other disease.

During my ten years of service as chief executive and claim committee chairman of a hospitalization company, it became increasingly apparent how very little the average layman knows about his heart. Your heart is a muscle about the size of a man's fist. It is a pump mechanism so expertly made that, if properly treated, it is capable of giving one hundred years of good service. Beating at an average of 70 strokes per minute, this organ will beat approximately 3.6 billion times in its life span. The healthy heart pumps and repumps daily approximately 10 tons of blood through 60,000 miles of arteries, veins, and capillaries. About 15 to 20 pounds of your life's blood must be circulated continuously by this sturdy organ.

Because heart disease is man's number one health enemy, your heart association, your insurance company, and the medical profession unite in urging you to adopt relaxed habits of living. Nonorganic heart maladies are brought on by worry, tension, strain, fatigue, and other abuses that disturb the heart's normal rhythm. You can protect and preserve this vital organ by taking your cue from it. The normal heart, working twenty-four hours each day, beats with regularity. But it also rests with regularity after each beat. To learn the habit of relaxed living, emulate your heart. Rest and relax between rounds, before your muscles become fatigued, overstrained, and overtense.

When tension affects your heart, you develop what the medical profession terms hypertension. This is your first warning. Get too excited and too tense too often, and up goes your blood pressure. Continue under pressure and soon you may experience shortness of breath and heart palpitations, accompanied by short paralyzing pains in the chest and left arm. Now you could have angina—and warning number two. Continue to overstrain your body and heart beyond your specific endurance limit, and the heart system breaks down and refuses its normal function. This is the third and, if not properly and promptly heeded, your last warning. You have a thrombosis or coronary occlusion. Now you *must* let up—or else.

Your doctor's diagnosis of thrombosis means that you have a clot or obstruction to the normal circulation of your blood. Or, if yours is a coronary occlusion, it usually means that the vessels of your heart are shut off from normal performance. Whatever the diagnosis, the very first thing to do after calling your doctor is to get into bed, get as comfortable as possible, and, unhurried, unworried, settle down to rest and relax.

By now your tension problem is critical. But even now it need not be fatal. Your doctor will probably keep you in bed for weeks or months, with instructions to remain quiet and relaxed. Here again your progress is largely up to you. Having had this final warning, you will try desperately to follow instructions. But try not to be too desperate. If you at last learn to relax you will probably live longer than if you hadn't had the attack. If not, your heart will kill you.

Why wait to learn your lesson the hard way? Watch out for you heart. Your imperative cue to slow down and relax is a feeling that you are getting tense. You cannot afford to misuse this reliable timepiece. If its mainspring snaps, so does your clock. Cultivate habits of relaxed living *before* your heart gets tired, strained, overtaxed, tense, and out of order. When you cultivate habits of relaxed living, your heart will be the first to know and relax with you.

Your mind will also know when you are relaxed. For when you relax you bring your whole being into balance. Suddenly you become aware that the whole world around you, which a moment before seemed upside down, is now in perfect balance also. If you are completely relaxed, your spirit will always reflect the inner peace you feel. If you feel serene, calm, quiet, and happy in a friendly, harmonious atmosphere of cheerfulness and goodwill toward mankind, everywhere—you are indeed relaxed.

And how do you get that way? The three-minute quiet period formula mentioned earlier in this chapter is the real secret. Once you learn how to use this secret periodically, you can then spend a lifetime perfecting its use. Use it often enough and you will live a healthier, happier, and probably longer life. Learn and use this secret. Accomplish this and you have captured, in three minutes, the essential purpose of this book.

You have learned some basic rules regarding tension. Don't abuse your eyes. Don't abuse your voice. And don't abuse your heart. They are tools that can help you build a calm, relaxed, and happy life. If they are improperly used they can destroy it. Think and relax. When you feel tension building, take a three-minute break. It can add happy years to your life.

SENSIBLE EXERCISE

The being we call man is the most perfect mechanism ever created. But, like things mechanical, it must be kept in use, greased, oiled, and properly repaired. The body of man needs exercise, good treatment, rest, relaxation, and freedom from that excessive friction we call tension. Tension is the sand in the oil that ruins your motor. Tension is the friction that grinds into the pores of your personality, settling in the most delicate, vulnerable spots and discoloring your whole outlook on life.

Complete neuromuscular release before, rather than after, tensions set in should be our constant aim. Prevention is much easier than cure. But to prevent tension, we must first recognize its approach and know how to sidestep and avoid it. How? You can avoid much of the muscular tension through proper exercise. Muscles, like talents, were given to us for use. And like the biblical talents, if we bury them and don't use them, they soon become cramped, rusty, corroded, and useless. Either we use or we lose them. It is an accepted medical fact that a perfectly healthy arm or leg, entirely immobilized and kept out of use long enough, eventually will become lifeless, atrophied, and incapable of use.

"We Americans are sitting pretty—too pretty—and too much," says the California Heart Association. "It's not just your heart muscles that need exercise, your whole body needs to be exercised and kept in trim, especially the legs." The Presidency of the United States is the most killing job in the world. Yet all our recent Presidents have found the time to exercise. President Eisenhower made the time to play enough golf to keep physically fit, and survived two massive heart attacks. President Kennedy, barred for a time from more strenuous exercise by a serious back injury, kept a rocking chair in his office. Tailor your exercise to your physical capabilities, but don't just sit on your veranda.

If you are a naturally athletic type, work out at home or in a gymnasium. If you feel up to it, jog—for miles or only around the block. Even if you have a serious heart condition your doctor will tell you that walking is excellent therapy. President Truman walked every morning of his life almost until his death at nearly ninety. Don't just sit there hour after hour, worrying or brooding. Inaction is one major cause of tension. Loosen up physically and you will loosen up mentally and emotionally.

Dr. Norman Vincent Peale said:

> One of the simplest ways to conquer life's irritations is by systematic relaxation. It's universally recognized that the mind has an enormous influence on the body; it is less often realized that the influence of the body on the mind is also important.
>
> A combined system of physical and mental relaxation involves loosening of muscle tensions and actually getting thoughts into a state of peacefulness. To accomplish this, sit loosely on a chair, resting hands palms down on the knees, fingers uncurled. Let your mind touch first upon one foot, then the other, conceiving of each as letting go, as relaxed.
>
> Proceed to relax the muscles of your legs, torso, arms, hands, neck, face and eyes in similar manner, consciously feeling them slackening as you would allow a rubber band to return to limpness.
>
> Remaining in this relaxed position, conceive of God saying in your ear, "Let not your heart be troubled." One thing is sure—irritations can't exist in the mind when it's filled with the peace of God.

Every man needs some form of exercise to soothe and calm his nerves. He needs to work with his own hands and sweat through his own pores. He needs to become physically tired occasionally, if he would successfully buck the tensions of daily living. As Tennyson put it, "A man must lose himself in action, lest he wither in despair." Just to dig in the garden or putter around the lawn will help. To tinker around the house, with the TV set, or the old jalopy, if you're a tinkerer, becomes a happy change of pace. Some like to hunt, fish, or swim. Others are skaters, skiers, or hikers.

Vacations are meant to be recreational relaxation, a real tension-relieving break in the year's tense and hectic activities. But many of us go to so much fuss in making the preparations to go that we create more tensions and frustrations than pleasure. And we travel at such a rapid, tense pace that when we finally return from a two-week vacation we require another two weeks to recuperate.

The old rocking chair is a mild form of exercise therapy and an excellent device for shedding your tensions and cares. People seldom get too old for rocker exercise. Country-style vacation resorts still feature relaxing rocking chairs as exercisers. The late President Kennedy's doctor prescribed the rocker therapy for his ailing back. Mothers rock children in their arms. Rocking seems to be one of nature's most tranquilizing exercises.

Here are seven exercises that may help keep you relaxed:

1. *Exercise your tonal qualities.* Speak softly. Talk slowly and gently in low, well-modulated tones. To strengthen your reserve power, speak as gently to people as to a baby or a puppy.

2. *Exercise your good judgment.* Watch your "bark." Don't growl, grumble, and grit your teeth. A clenched jaw can cause tension. Remember to use often the five magic phrases that never ruffle and that usually get results.

These are: if you please; thank you; may I help?; I'm proud of you; and, what is your opinion?

3. *Exercise self-control.* Never talk when angry, never eat when angry, and never go to bed when angry. Make a conscious effort never to get angry in the first place. Anger burns up your energy, raises your blood pressure, poisons your system, and deadens your brain.

4. *Exercise your patience.* If you must blow off steam, at least wait until you're quite alone. Don't let an out-of-control person goad you into the same folly. One at a time is bad enough, but when two persons lose their heads at the same time, all is lost.

5. *Exercise your tongue,* but in moderation. Talk, but talk sense. Keep skid chains on your tongue. Hear no evil, see no evil, and, especially, speak no evil. A poisoned, spiteful, gossipy, irresponsible tongue is a two-edged sword of destruction. The tongue is a muscle that needs exercise, but as that great surgeon, the late Dr. Charles Stanley White, once said: "The tongue is the longest, most dangerous muscle in the human body."

6. *Exercise your heartstrings* with charity, compassion, empathy, and consideration for others. Practice being too nearsighted to see the unlovely. Overlook the dust on your hostess' table when enjoying the hospitality of her household. Ignore the squeak in your neighbor's gate and admire the roses in his garden.

7. *Exercise your soul.* Stop. Pause for poise and power. Form the habit of pausing for brief intervals. When you feel yourself getting tense and jumpy, take time out, stop dead in your tracks and rest briefly. This is exercise in the therapy of quietude.

Look. With eyes closed, we sometimes see more than when they're wide open. So take a good look at yourself through your mind's eye. Close your eyes, rule out all selfishness, greed, noise, haste, and disharmony. For sixty seconds, substitute spiritual consciousness for consciousness of self. Muse, meditate, and count your blessings. Listen. Now that you're quiet and still, and in a relaxed mood, listen for the music of silence. For sixty seconds, don't think, don't move—just listen. Seek the harmony and rhythm of God's universe. When you've learned to listen, you've found a priceless treasure. Nurse it. Nurture it. Let it develop and grow. For to be at peace, to be quiet, still, serene, calm, and composed is to be attuned to the Infinite, where all is peace and there is no tension.

MENTAL TENSION AND MENTAL ILLNESS

This is an age of anxiety, of confusion, and of all kinds of tension. People are fearful, harassed, and emotionally upset. Tension headaches, emotional disturbance, mental health, and psychiatry have become casual household phrases. Doctors and laymen speak loosely in terms of anxiety neuroses, nervous hypertension, therapeutic relaxation, progressive relaxation, residual tensions, paranoia. Mental health has become an American conversation piece and a major industry.

This is the day of the psychologist, the psychiatrist, and the psychoanalyst. The psychologist specializes in the science and study of the mental processes and behavior of man and of animals. The psychiatrist is an M.D. with training in the field of emotional illness. The psychoanalyst is a psychiatrist with additional training in tracing repressed instinctual drives and bringing into awareness the origin and effect of emotional conflicts with the hope of eliminating or diminishing them.

It has been well said that the psychopath creates dream castles, the neurotic lives in them, and the psychiatrist collects the rent. Constant emphasis on mankind's emotional tendencies may be planting in already weak minds the seeds of greater emotional stress. Man doesn't need further impediments to his emotional equilibrium. Our lives are so confused and twisted that at times we tend to get the wrong perspective. Why let confused people get us more confused? We tend to fear more than we hurt. Under an unwise barrage of questionable propaganda about mental health, man is prone to become more tense rather than more relaxed.

Many of us are like the salesman asleep in his Pullman berth during a night train wreck. Awakened by the sudden crash and the bumping of wheels on the roadbed, he dressed hurriedly in the now totally dark Pullman, getting his pants on hind part before. Just then his coach overturned, throwing him through the window and down over the bank, where he lay momentarily stunned. As he regained consciousness, a rescue worker leaned over him with a flashlight and asked, "Sir, are you badly hurt?" "No, I don't hurt very much." Then, glancing down at his hind-part-before pants, he continued, "But I'm sure horribly twisted out of shape." People who are twisted up mentally often are like that train-wrecked salesman. Constant tension and turmoil can make confused wrecks out of normal people.

Mental illness is far more insidious, less understood, and much more difficult to treat than any physical impairment. However, it is not the purpose of this book to deal with serious mental illness or psychological therapy.

This chapter points up the problem of mental tension and attempts to help the reader to do something about it for himself. Tensions left uncontrolled can become chronic, developing into a serious mental illness. Tension tendencies can be averted, avoided, and/or corrected pleasantly. The individual needs only to exercise good judgment and act while there is still time. It is up to each of us to stand on his own two feet and think for himself. Many so-called experts stand on intellectual feet of clay. These are the ones who often are prone to rationalize, explain away, and excuse every type of infraction of the laws of God and man by some synthetic fabrication of psycho-clairvoyance that they think only they possess. That everybody's-crazy-but-me complex exists everywhere.

Taking the new doctor on an inspection tour of the mental hospital, the nurse pointed to a patient standing erect in bed, in a high silk hat, with a hand inside his pajama coat, and said, "That one thinks he's Napoleon, and that God gave him that hat." The patient seated on the next bed said, "Nurse, he *is* Napoleon—but I certainly did not give him my hat."

Unquestionably, of all man's problems, the tense mind is the most common, perhaps the most serious, and certainly the most difficult to treat. Man's greatest problem is himself. No man can afford to go through life all wrapped up in himself and his problems. Too much "I" strain is both selfish and suicidal.

The individual must learn to diagnose and prescribe for his own condition. Once you understand and thoroughly appreciate the cause of tensions—physical, mental and spiritual—you can proceed to correct them—if you have the will to do so. And once you master the technique of mental relaxation, mental stress will soon subside. Medi-

cal science has aptly demonstrated that emotional imbalance causes many physical ailments. The doctor and
his skills have done much to alleviate physical suffering
and to help those who tend to go out of mental control.
But your future mental health depends more upon your
own attitude and actions than upon any outside help.
If only we could learn to relax, control ourselves and our
little minds, we would soon solve our own tension problems and forget all about mental health. Man needs to
relax all over, mentally, physically, and spiritually.

One pregnant woman became so distraught and tense
over a pending minor operation for her young son that she
lost her unborn baby. Fear caused tension and resulted
in a spontaneous miscarriage. Another woman with fail-
ing vision, already full of fear and apprehension, got so
tense on being told by her doctor that eventually she
would be blind, that she lost her sight even while the
doctor was talking. Her doctor's face was the last thing
she ever saw.

Man is prone to psychogenic disorders. His emotional
conflicts may produce bodily disease. An emotional problem, left unchecked, can blossom into a mental problem
of serious proportions. Mental tension is hypnotic. It so
distorts your mental processes that you cannot think
straight, see clearly, or hear acutely. And wrong thinking,
with negative attitudes, is largely responsible for much
of man's nervous tensions. Emotional strain can so paralyze your muscular activities that a physical and nervous
breakdown may occur.

The whole theory of psychoanalysis is based upon the
therapeutic power of ideas and words. Sometimes it helps
lessen our anxieties and tensions if we get part of the

weight of the problem off our chest by talking it over with someone. Whether that someone is a professional or not isn't too important—if he is intellectually perceptive in these areas. You need not be an expert to help. Dr. Harry Levinson, director of mental health of the Menninger Foundations, said: "Listening is the key to helping a person who is emotionally distressed. If you want to help someone who is anxious and upset, the trick is to be a good listener." He gave four suggestions: Don't interrupt. Don't belittle the problem. Don't be impatient, hear him out. And don't provide the answers. The role of the listener is to serve as a sounding board. The troubled person, unless he is too ill to do so, must come to his own decisions.

Therapeutic relaxation is the means of liberating the victim from pathological fears, friction, distress, and disaster-thinking. It is good mental therapy if you can guide yourself, or another, away from these negative concepts to a more optimistic road. You can crowd out unhealthy negative thoughts of frustration, failure, and disaster by positive thinking—if you will. Why shorten your life with needless tensions, mental or otherwise? If you can think and act with optimism, you will not be troubled with mental tension. To avoid mental tension, be concerned with things as they are, rather than as they might be. Live in the present tense—facing today with optimism, without regret for any yesterday and without worry about some future tomorrow. Many have found the Twenty-third Psalm to be a great source of self-help. For years it has been the author's favorite hitching post in times of tension. For the convenience of the reader, the Twenty-third Psalm is here recorded:

The Lord is my shepherd, I shall not want.
He maketh me to lie down in green pastures;
He leadeth me beside the still waters.
He restoreth my soul.
He leadeth me in the path of righteousness for
    His name's sake.
Yea, though I walk through the valley of the
    shadow of death,
I will fear no evil; for Thou art with me;
Thy rod and Thy staff they comfort me.
Thou preparest a table before me in the presence of
    mine enemies.
Thou anointest my head with oil;
My cup runneth over.
Surely, goodness and mercy shall follow me all the
    days of my life,
And I will dwell in the house of the Lord forever.

If you will read and repeat the psalm aloud until you understand it; then teach your mind to lie down in green pastures of hope and optimistic faith; if you can visualize and lead your spirit beside the still waters of quietude and peace; then tension and friction can light no fuse of neurotic dynamite within your heart and brain. For peace and serenity, like fear and tension, start in the minds and hearts of men. If there is peace in the inner man, then there is no room for mental tension.

YOU AND YOUR ATTITUDE

You are the sum total of what you believe. The world is a looking glass that gives back to you not only the reflection of your own face, but your personality and actions. Your attitude often is more important than your ability. Your attitude determines how well you maintain your emotional and intellectual equilibrium. It is the balance wheel of your actions and reactions. Individual personality is a combination of personal traits, tendencies, attitudes, and habits. Why then do sensible human beings tend to be so negative? Why do men deliberately and persistently kick themselves? Why doubt our abilities? Why mark ourselves down? Why grow fearful, apprehensive, and tense? Why do so many become compliant neurotics—too dopey to develop right attitudes and too apathetic to try? Why allow the poisonous weeds of a negative attitude to choke out an otherwise positive personality? Why grow personality weeds when flowers and fruits can be cultivated just as easily? Why not encourage positive personality-building attitudes, traits, tendencies, and habits that blossom into a sane, mature, relaxed personality?

"We speak of nervous breakdowns," says Dr. Murray Banks, in *How to Live with Yourself,* "but nerves never break down. The weakness is not our nerves but our habits of adjustment. We break down as an avenue of escape from reality." We simply fail to develop right personality muscles. Problems we will always have. Men will always face the possibility of loss, failure, old age, and death. But why concentrate on fear until we pyramid a cramp into a calamity? Apprehensions only breed a nervous stomach, a weak heart, and a tension headache.

You are the pilot of your own ship. Allow yourself to become upset and depressed with every problem, expecting the worst, and you will surely find it. Give way to melancholy and soon you will be shipwrecked on the shoals of despair. You can whine and cry over life's struggles until you crack up mentally and physically. Unfortunately, many people spend their lives emphasizing their ills, difficulties, and problems. Tension-packed days and sleepless nights do not just happen. You can nurse an inferiority complex until you actually become inferior. We are prone to magnify our hurts and our lacks until they become obsessions. Irrational attitudes distort your perspective. Self-pity, anxieties, tensions, and neurotic tendencies can ruin your health, your happiness, and your life. Dr. Maurice S. Goldstein of Michael Reese Hospital in Chicago said, "Investigations have shown repeatedly that disease or death can come from an individual's emotional overresponse to some new and challenging situation." Dr. David McRioch, psychiatrist at Walter Reed Army Hospital, tells of American soldiers drowning in two feet of water after having received slight flesh wounds when allied forces landed in Normandy on D-Day, June 6, 1944. You can let an emotional flesh wound carry you down to despair. Negative attitudes drag you to the bottom, while a confident, positive attitude of always expecting and deserving the best guides you to higher ground.

Be thankful that our habits, traits, tendencies, and attitudes, good or bad, all are learned and therefore can be unlearned. Undesirable ones can be discarded and new ones learned. If you have a generous, optimistic outlook on life, you probably acquired the trait from parents or others who convinced you, either by example or advice, of the merits of such qualities. Unconsciously we imitate the good or bad that we see in others. The person who is hostile and suspicious and negative-minded probably acquired that unfortunate viewpoint from someone or something that convinced him that only through hostility and suspicion and negativeness could he survive in a hostile and cruel world.

If you are not now a serene, relaxed person—change. Develop new personality muscles. Drop your wrong attitudes and learn new ones—right ones. It is just that simple: Decide—then do. The transition need not be unpalatable or unpleasant. Your emotional habits, your mental attitude, your physical posture—all can be changed gradually and pleasantly. You need not hold your nose and swallow the whole dose at one big gulp. Sip it slowly. Change bit by bit. Reorganize your life on a constructive pattern of rational, positive behavior. Soon you'll find you've already let go. You'll be untense. You will have dropped neurotic, irrational tendencies. And you will be relaxed. Positive attitudes, tendencies, traits, and habits, consistently practiced, soon become a part of a relaxed personality. Eventually the subconscious takes over and thereafter reflects automatically the knowledge and experience learned.

If we change the inner attitudes of the mind, we can change the outer aspects of our lives. All we need do is substitute new habits for old ones, right ones for wrong. How? Select new ideas, a new environment, new attitudes, even new associates if necessary. Abandon the negative and substitute the positive. By controlling his attitude, an individual controls his whole life. A person with an attitude of seeking only to serve cannot be filled with anxiety for self. A person with a deep religious conviction cannot be overcome by worry. A deep abiding faith blots out fear and tension and frustration.

Think it over. Doesn't it make sense to stop fighting windmills in your mind? Every time you feel yourself getting tense, stop, look, and listen. Say "Whoa!" to yourself. Then look at the tenseness. Examine it. See *why* you are letting your mind and your emotions churn painfully and needlessly. If it is fear, look at what you are afraid of. Listen to the voice of reason within yourself. It will tell you how foolish and stupid you are to let nameless dreads and needless worries distort your reason and erode your efficiency and your health. Whatever your problem may be, getting tense about it will only magnify it. Realize that it is your *attitude* toward the problem and not the problem itself that is getting you tense. You cannot throw out the problem, but you can certainly change your attitude toward it, and with the proper attitude you can either overcome the problem or accept it and work toward overcoming it.

Admit that you and your problems are not that important in the scheme of things. A few wrinkles or a receding hairline have put aging movie stars into mental institutions. Think about it. Are they really that important? Of course not. And neither is your problem, even though it may be much more serious. If it involves another person, try to talk it out with him. If it is within yourself, talk about it with yourself or a disinterested friend. You will find that it is your attitude toward the problem that is causing the unwanted and unnecessary tension. Change your attitude. You can do it. You learned the wrong attitudes that have made you tense. You can learn the right attitudes that will make you relaxed.

3

Don't
Self-Destruct

FIGHTING FEAR

Fear is man's greatest weakness. All of us experience
fears and phobias of some kind. Fear is man's greatest
enemy. It robs him of his normal faculties. Fear is sand
in the machinery of the mind. Fear kills ambition, crip-
ples talent, and dims the intellect. Fear deadens our finer
sensibilities, warps the personality, and petrifies the
spirit. Yet fear is only a shadow, a mirage, a fake. So
why let any phony fear fool you?

How can we successfully deal with our fears? "Do the
thing you fear," said Ralph Waldo Emerson. The individual is as small as the little things he fears, says the
psychologist. Crowd out fear with faith, says the philosopher, for courage is not absence of fear but triumph over
it. But, if you cannot eliminate your fears entirely, don't

despair. You can rise above, avoid, reduce, or conquer your fears through intellect and willpower, courage and faith. Here are some of the suggestions of experts.

1. *Admit your fears.* Honest confession is good for the spirit. The moment you recognize and admit your fears, the battle is half won. Every human has both a hero and a coward within his makeup. To admit his fear is an act of courage. It takes courage to admit a weakness. It takes even more courage to admit our fears before others. But to smother, hide, and condone our weaknesses simply adds the fear of exposure to our load. So, why not recognize your fear for the hypocrite and fraud that it is? "Of all the liars in the world," said Rudyard Kipling, "sometimes the worst are your fears."

Fear is an insidious thief that sneaks up on our blind side and robs us in the dark. It makes weaklings of the strong. Ninety-eight percent of life's troubles are imaginary—and most are caused by fear. An infant is born with only two basic fears—the fear of falling and the fear of noise. But soon he acquires or is taught algophobia (fear of pain). Gradually a miscellaneous assortment of some 7,000 additional fears is added. To keep yours from growing in size and number, start choking them off now, by recognizing and admitting them. That is step number one.

2. *Assess your fears* at face value. Immunize yourself against the vicious virus of fear by good old common sense. Fear grows out of doubt, anxiety, confusion, indecision, and negative thinking. Don't let any fear psychosis stampede your mind and body into frustration and failure. Remember, you can only go into the woods halfway—the rest of the time you are coming out. "Reconcile yourself to the worst that can happen to you, then try to

improve on that worst," said Dale Carnegie," and you will have little cause for fear or worry."

In *Release from Nervous Tensions,* David Harold Fink, M.D., said, "Fear is both physical and mental. It is a compound of physical and mental processes. It's more than what you feel. It's what you do with your entire body. It isn't physical pain we fear so much as the thought of it. Almost always the fear is greater than the pain itself."

"Fear," said Saint Francis of Sales, "is a greater pain than pain itself." And the French essayist Michel de Montaigne once said, "Who feareth to suffer, suffereth already, because he feareth." You can be sure your fears will foul you up unless you find the judgment and courage to root them out.

Fear and nervous tension can upset your digestive system, cause loss of appetite, and produce all kinds of aches, pains, and discomfort. A simple tooth extraction, unreasonably delayed through fear, can poison the body and do irreparable harm. Optometrists tell us that fear can distort vision and has been known to cause total blindness. Doctors say that heart trouble is often functional or symptomatic, not organic; that fear produces nervous palpitation, high blood pressure, and heart strain.

Fear causes your heart to beat more rapidly and to skip. That makes you uncomfortable and nervous. With increased concern comes heart strain. It is a vicious cycle. The more you give way to fear, the more you injure your body and thus cause more fear and more injury. Medical science tells us that 92 percent of peptic ulcers and 85 percent of colitis cases are attended by the emotional strain of fear. Fear and emotional imbalance cause tension headache, skin disorders, diarrhea, and a hundred other diseases and seemingly unrelated illnesses.

Man is literally beset by fears. We fear the dark, the unknown, the strange, and the unexpected. Some fear pain. Others, sickness and disease. Some are afraid of dead bodies, storms, fires, crowds. Others suffer fear of going insane, being unwanted, alone, or unloved. Often our fears are ridiculous, irrational, and needlessly devastating. Yet to the victim they are vital and real. Each must learn to rationalize and overcome his own phobia.

3. *Beat your fears to the punch.* Under control, your emotional nervous system can drive you on to greater achievement. Out of control, it can wreck your life. A good defense is a prompt offense, says the military. "Do the thing you fear," said Emerson and Carnegie. "The only thing we have to fear is fear itself," said Franklin D. Roosevelt. And if Dr. Stanley Jones's theory is correct, your admission of fear and decision to act positively in spite of it disposes of 90 percent of the problem without firing a single shot. So why concern yourself over that other 10 percent?

In a recent survey ten top athletes, when asked: "How do you control your fears and tensions under pressure?" agreed on these three basic rules: (a) Be ready, prepared, practiced and expect to win. (b) Be sure, self-confident, without inhibitions, and with plenty of willpower, backed up by reserve power. (c) Be relaxed. Don't be overanxious. Take one step at a time. Do your best and leave the rest in the lap of the gods.

4. *Develop automatic reflexes.* Fear is wrong-believing, second-guessing, and negative indecision. Decide and act. And once your decision is made, keep your mind away from defeatism. Keep your batteries charged with positive thoughts and your reaction will be both positive and automatic. If you fear thunder and lightning, don't hide

your head under a pillow. Force yourself to look out into the storm. If you fear the dark, walk alone in the dark until your fears subside. Act boldly and the ghost that lurks around the corner in the darkness will take care of itself, automatically.

I know. It happened to me in my youth. Our family had moved from our little farm along the railroad to a village house and store that Dad had purchased. We didn't want tramps to move into the old farmhouse and it was decided that I, a twelve-year-old boy, should sleep out there until it was sold. To this day I don't know who made that decision. I'm quite sure I wasn't consulted. I was petrified with fear each night as I walked out that dark road, alone except for the crickets and hoot owls. One pitch-black night, as I neared the vacant house, I heard someone jump and run from the front porch. And believe it or not, I was so excited and shocked that I ran after him, yelling bloody murder. The worst had happened and I had won. After that I was no longer afraid.

5. *Talk over your fears.* Inoculate yourself against fear attacks. One way is to immunize yourself before the disease takes over. Here an ounce of prevention proves truly worth a pound of cure.

To discuss your problems and fears with someone, even if it is only with yourself, can be helpful. Always remember that fear is a cesspool of festering bacteria that can't stand the light of reason. So air your fears, expose these microbes to the fresh air of logical scrutiny, rational analysis, and discussion. Talk over your fears with another. Two heads are better than one, even though one remains silent. Your neighbor need not make a suggestion, or even say a word. If you talk the problem over aloud, you will better understand it yourself. And as better understanding comes, fears will go.

6. *Build a positive approach through courage.* Ernest Hemingway once said, "Courage is grace under pressure." Ward off the arrows of fear by building a positive fence of courage. Courage is the intelligent, scientific approach to life. Courage is a built-in radarlike signal, called faith. Courage and faith control our reserve units that rush up reinforcements of backbone when the enemy—fear—attacks. Courage is a wall of faith so strong that it crowds out fear.

You can't lose any bout with fear if you will learn and constantly practice this three-way philosophy of practical faith: (a) Trust yourself, secure always in the knowledge that you are doing your best. Be sure you are, then relax. For no one having done his best ever has cause to fear or worry. (b) Trust your fellowman—and live so that you may merit and reasonably expect his implicit trust in you. (c) Trust your Maker—for if you believe deeply in the Infinite and subscribe to the thesis of ultimate triumph of right over wrong, doing your part to make it happen, then your faith will warm your own heart, inspire confidence in others, and breed the courage to face up to any problem, unafraid.

THE STUPIDITY OF WORRY

Worry is the misshapen little brother of fear. Why worry? Why borrow trouble? Why cry over spilled milk? Why are people so prone to worry despite the fact that both statistics and common sense tell us that worry is not only futile and foolish but harmful? Why worry, when 90 percent of the things we worry about never happen, many turn out to be blessings in disguise, some already have happened, and few ever are as bad as we feared?

There are two things not to worry about—those things you cannot do, and those things you can do. Worry is the excessive rate of interest we pay for borrowed trouble. It is mountain-climbing over molehills. It is looking down, not up. The worrier lives in the shadows instead of reaching for the silver lining that always lurks behind the dark clouds. Worry, even over legitimate causes for concern, always does more harm than good. What possible good can it do to fret and worry over what can't be helped? And why should any rational person worry over past events?

Many of our worries come from crossing bridges before we come to them; but why do we persist in anticipating trouble? This negative mental attitude spawns the very trouble it envisions. Never forget that any person who does the best he can has little cause to worry, least of all over success or lack of it.

What good are gold, prestige, and power when that panel turns up with your name on it? What shall it profit a man if he gains world acclaim but meanwhile loses his own health, happiness, and peace of mind? Time has a way of healing. Dark clouds pass away. Problems often solve themselves. As a test, try to remember all the things you worried about only yesterday. Try it, and see the absolute folly of senseless worry. The rational person will remember that today is the tomorrow he worried about yesterday, that yesterday died last night, and that tomorrow is a brand-new day. Looking back, were your problems really as formidable as envisioned? And did your worry help?

Fortunately for us, our burdens seldom become too heavy to bear, especially if we lay our load down at close of day and relax. After a night of rest and refreshment of body, mind, and spirit, the picture takes on a brighter hue with each new dawn. Expect the best, instead of the worst, and walk with confidence, one step at a time. Confucius said, "A journey of a thousand miles begins with a single step." Remember that today is the first day of the rest of your life.

Too much tension, fear, and worry can knock the individual off his feet, off his feed, and off his rocker. Worry bacteria find a fertile field in the empty heads and frustrated minds of the starved and anemic spirits of those of little faith. "God forgive us for our ulcers," said the late minister and Senate chaplain, Peter Marshall, "they're indicative of the small measure of our faith." Why aren't we more sensible? Why don't we put our worries away? Men of goodwill live and let live, give instead of grab, and relax instead of worry.

Why must we rant, rave, rush and fret, lie and covet, cheat and steal? Why do we depart from sensible, legitimate pursuits and treat with each other like predatory animals instead of like rational men and women? The worrier makes mountain-climbing over molehills his favorite pastime. He sees a dust cloud and expects a tornado. His vision is distorted. He looks at pygmies and sees twelve-foot giants. He strangles over a gnat as though it were a camel.

A stray hair by its continual irritation may give more annoyance than a sharp blow. Why waste five dollars' worth of concern on a five-cent problem? Keep in mind the arithmetic of senseless worry. Think of the possible dollar-and-cents cost of lost efficiency, lost prestige, lost friendship, loss of face, and ultimate loss of health. A pound of lead weighs no more than a pound of feathers. It only seems heavier. "I'm an old man," said the sage, "and have suffered many troubles which have never happened." My dentist assured me, "Even false teeth have advantages." Rebelling momentarily over a mouthful of new china clippers, I challenged him to name one. With a grin and an understanding pat on the arm he said, "Now you can whistle while you brush them."

Worry causes more ills than all the diseases since Adam. Worry is a disease that saps your initiative and feeds on your energy, as it literally eats into your life like acid. The word *worry* is derived from an Anglo-Saxon word meaning to strangle or choke. That is exactly what worry does to its victim. It chokes off his normal intellect, strangles his ambition, and generally weakens his physical body as it spreads and deepens and feeds on itself.

Ulcers seldom come from what you eat or don't eat. More often they come from what's eating you. Inner discord creates the worry climate of ulcer gulch in which disharmony and despair thrive. When worry grates on the nervous system long enough, it causes acid secretions that in turn cause ulcers. This acidity corrodes and eats out the stomach lining, causing great sore spots or ulcers to form. Gastric ulcers cause the stomach to turn cannibal and eat itself. Medical statistics indicate that stomach ulcers rank as the tenth-highest cause of death in the United States annually. According to conservative estimates, there are 7 million present-day ulcer victims, with 12 percent of our total population headed for this affliction. And the majority of them owe it all to worry and tension.

Worry is contagious. Once it gets a foothold, it spreads its nervous distemper, not only in the victim but into the life of everyone it touches. It spawns harmful words and actions that seldom can be recalled. It results in unhappy lives and wrecked homes. It makes the hearts of loved ones ache in futile helplessness. But some people seem to enjoy being miserable. They get joy in bumping their heads against the wall. And almost always they carry others along with them.

"A busy man who doesn't know how to fight worry will die young," said Dr. Alexis Carrel. If you worry for long, you become less intelligent, less capable, and less effective. As tension increases, the victim gets more panicky and irrational. Increased apprehension leads to a vicious cycle. The more the tension, the more he worries and grows still more tense, until eventually something has to give. Unquestionably worry is the root cause of many of our problems. Of all the human frailties that keep normal men and women from relaxing, worry is the most prevalent, the most insidious, the most harmful, and the most useless.

Worry responds poorly to scientific or medical treatment. In fact, it is the one disease that the victim alone can cure. Or perhaps not alone. The solution includes positive attitudes, habits, and actions of body, mind, and spirit. Here are a few specific and helpful suggestions to choke off worry before it gets to be an incurable habit:

1. *Keep busy,* for the idle hours are the treacherous hours. And start now. Indecision and procrastination breed confusion and negative-mindedness, the climate in which worry spawns and spreads and destroys.

2. *Have a plan.* Dale Carnegie said, "Everybody worries about something." The solution, he said, is "first to determine the worst that can happen, reconcile yourself to that worst, then set out immediately to improve upon it." Industrialist Charles Kettering once said, "A problem well stated is a problem half solved." Both Carnegie and Kettering recommend this four-step formula for problem-solving: (a) Write out the problem; (b) Write out all the possible solutions; (c) Select the one solution you consider best; (d) Start at once to put it into effect.

3. *Take stock.* Inventory your assets. Don't mark yourself down. Why kick yourself needlessly? You may be better than you think. Most people find this to be true when a fair appraisal of talents is made.

4. *Do your best.* Expect the best. Deserve the best. Then go out and get it. No one can do more. And no one having done his best has cause to worry. Furthermore, that best will grow better as fear and worry are replaced by faith and action.

5. *Compare.* It helps just to look about us as we travel along. Shed a silent tear for the mourners in a funeral procession. Note the tenderness of the stranger helping the sightless man across the street. Have a heart and remember, "There, but for the grace of God, go I." Everyone has some problem, some cross to bear. To see the heavier load on another's back must make us ashamed of our petty worries. Counting our blessings instead of our problems is a surefire inoculation against the worry sickness.

6. *Get involved.* Think more about others and less about yourself. Help your neighbor. It's good for him and good therapy for you.

7. *Try religion.* An inner peace and tranquillity of mind

and heart are prerequisites for avoiding worry. True religion should bring this result. It is the primary business of your religion to let God help carry your burdens through each day. There's nothing—absolutely nothing—that you and God can't handle together. Stamp out fear and worry by putting your faith to work. When you feel the forces of fear and worry sweeping over you, that's the time to begin a counterattack of faith.

What a happy, relaxed, and wonderful world this would be if more people attempted honestly to live by the Golden Rule, the Sermon on the Mount, and the Commandments. If each of us had more concern for the rights of others, extended ourselves more fully in service to mankind, obeyed the laws of God and man, and labored to bring more of the spirit of the Kingdom of Heaven down to earth, we'd have less time or cause or inclination to worry. We'd be happier, healthier, and more relaxed.

THE FOOLISHNESS OF ANGER

"He that is soon angry dealeth foolishly," said Solomon. "He that is slow to anger is better than the mighty; and he that ruleth his spirit than he that taketh a city." The poet William Blake said, "Anger is a poison tree." And Charles Baxter, a financial expert and industrial engineer of the 1950s, said, "A man's venom poisons himself more than his victim."

Anger can literally burn and corrode you, both inside and out. Men truthfully say, "I was burned up . . . I was so mad that I couldn't see . . . I couldn't half talk . . . I couldn't even think . . . I was fit to be tied . . . It just made me sick." Anger can make you blind in more ways than one. It can numb your lips, paralyze your brain, tie you in emotional knots, and literally make you ill. Every time we give way to violent anger we seriously disturb the proper functioning of the organs of our bodies.

Why do otherwise intelligent people foolishly give way to temper? Why do we indulge in such absurd, stupid behavior? Temper often is acquired because of lack of intelligent restraint. A selfish overemphasis on problems and tensions can continue until angry outbursts become a habit. "The instant we feel anger," said the historian Thomas Carlyle, "we have already ceased striving for truth and have begun striving for self. . . . Discussion is an exchange of intelligence, while angry outbursts are an exchange of ignorance."

One hothead partially excuses his outbursts by saying afterward, "I get mad fast but cool off quickly." But a display of temper isn't that easily excused. Quick recovery helps save face. And certainly, not to carry a grudge or harbor resentment is a virtue, but temper scars remain. Once a man allows his temper to boil over and explode in impulsive and violent anger toward another, the two seldom can return to the same easy, relaxed, friendly basis. Apology and forgiveness help, but memory scars heal slowly.

Temper can be controlled if we work at it, but the road isn't easy. Here are some simple rules to help us avoid temper explosions:

1. *Don't provoke anger needlessly* in yourself or another. Especially, don't tease children. It may prove amusing for the moment but do irreparable harm to a budding personality in the formative stages.

2. *Don't tolerate anger in yourself.* Choke your temper tendencies. If you carry a chip on your shoulder, you

pay through the nose. Your anger and ill-will breed hatred, which cannot long be concealed or contained, and hatred is even more vicious than anger. Anger shows in your face, your eyes, your voice, and your attitude. If you are full of animosity toward me, I sense your hostility and automatically respond in kind.

3. *Don't be upset by trifles,* and don't let little things irritate and anger you. Why allow yourself to become all hot and bothered over nothing? When you begin to stew in anger, turn off the gas, for a boiling temper can cook your goose.

4. *Don't lose your temper—use it.* Righteous indignation may be a good thing. But first be sure it is righteous. Uncontrolled anger is a boomerang that returns to explode on its own launching pad. An angry blast can sear the flamethrower. According to the late Dr. E. Stanley Jones, "The person who loses his temper digs a grave for the person he might have been and falls into it," and "Anyone who angers you, conquers you."

5. *Don't shoot from the hip.* An irate constituent hastily wired his senator, "To hell with you and your stupid ideas. Offensive letter follows," only to learn later that the senator had been misquoted. Eating crow is neither palatable nor easy. It is better to look before leaping in anger. Develop patience and tolerance instead of irritability and anger.

6. *Build your own shock absorber* against sudden and unexpected annoyances. When the air gets tense, some people pause. Some laugh it off or count to ten, or change the subject, or make a speedy exit. Whatever the method, it pays to have a built-in emergency escape plan.

One sales manager had a most effective strategy. When a salesman got fighting mad in his presence, he would laugh loud and long. In fact, he'd keep it up until it got silly. The irate salesman frequently would end up laughing at his manager's undignified tactics—and perhaps at himself. Suddenly the manager would stop laughing and become quietly serious. Then, after a long pause, he'd say, "Okay, let's talk about it later . . . meanwhile, we both can think about it some more . . . we'll work something out." With that the interview was over. And usually the problem would get solved without further display of temper.

7. *Never make an important decision in anger.* When infuriated, we tend to become illogical, irrational, and confused. Anger often causes us to say and do things we don't really mean. We can apologize, but we can never quite take back those angry words.

A congressman got excited about a political opponent during a radio speech and said, "Why that dumb ox ought to be kicked to death by a jackass." Then, quickly regaining his sense of humor, he added, "And, by golly, maybe I'm the one that ought to do it."

8. *Don't read anything important when angry or upset.* It isn't called blind anger for nothing. The victim who goes into a rage can't see clearly, for tension and anger dim his vision.

9. *Never speak when angry.* Words spoken in anger become a two-edged sword that cuts both ways. Speak when you're angry, and you'll make the best speech you'll ever regret.

10. *Don't go to bed angry.* Never try to go to sleep in an angry mood. You won't sleep well and you won't like your dreams. Don't nurse your anger and animosity at bedtime. Don't let angry fires smolder as you try to slumber. "Never let the sun go down on your wrath"—Ephesians 4:26.

11. *Never eat when angry.* Undue emotional upset, and anger in particular, temporarily impair or destroy your digestive processes.

12. *Don't let anger get away from you.* When you feel it building up, pull that choke leash. If let run wild, anger can make you so numb of tongue and brain that you neither speak nor think straight. As you rant and rave, you get more jumpy and irrational by the minute.

Anger is physically harmful. Your heartbeat increases and your blood vessels become strained under increased pressure. Fatal strokes can come from anger when a blood vessel bursts in the brain. "Anger is thought to be the emotion most harmful to the heart," says Dr. Theodore van Dellen. "No one wants to join the coronary club. But almost every day we see people do all the silly things that pave the way for membership . . . engage in a quarrel . . . argue over trivialities . . . these emotional outbreaks are not going unnoticed by the old ticker."

Don't get so boiling mad that you suffer a crippling heart attack. Bury your temper before it buries you. A bank official in Maryland got so angry and tense over petty disagreements with a fellow officer that he suffered a stroke that took his life.

When another person gets angry, don't you, too. Life is filled with tense situations. Tempers flare and harsh words are spoken. So long as you don't get angry, too, you're safe. For if one person at a time gets mad, it is regrettable; but if both parties fly off the handle at once, that can be disastrous. If you want your marriage or your business life to be a success, one partner must keep his head when the fireworks start. Let it be you. All of us are human. There will inevitably be times when someone with whom you're involved builds up a head of emotional steam. That's the time to watch your bark.

There are at least two times when it is best to keep silent. One is when you are so angry that if you do speak you'll say something you'd regret later. The other is when the other fellow is so obviously in a fit of temper that no matter what you say, it will be of little help.

13. *Don't bottle up your anger.* Try to explain reasonably what has caused it. Prolonged silence just to avoid the issue can be dangerous. Prolonging a misunderstanding only makes it more difficult to settle. If you're wrong, quickly admit it. If it is the other fellow, try to help him save face.

14. *Set the example.* It is a demonstrable fact that you can largely control the other person's actions by your own. Scientific tests prove conclusively that you can control the other person's tone of voice by your own voice. When a person is shouted at, he will almost always respond with the same degree of loudness.

How you say a thing often is more important than what you say. Much friction in life results from the tone of the voice—"A soft answer turneth away wrath." Furthermore, it is a proven fact that if you keep your voice soft, you are not likely to become angry. Of course, that isn't easy. Anyone can smile when skies are blue and things are going his way. But to remain calm and serene when you have every reason to get boiling mad is the trick. We admire the individual who can do it.

When a customer exploded unreasonably, one successful salesman paused so long that both became embarrassed. Then, quietly and calmly, with a smile from the heart out, he said, "Gosh—I thought for a moment that I was going to lose *my* temper. That would have been a

foolish thing to do, wouldn't it?" The pause and the salesman's unexpected reaction in taking the blame himself
allowed the customer time to regain his composure. As a
consequence, the tension was relieved and a business
contact saved. His name is long since forgotten, but his
kindness I shall ever remember.

15. *Use diplomacy.* Tempers flare and normal courtesy
disappears quickly when people sit behind the wheel of a
car. A car often transforms a polished diplomat into a
raving savage. Two cars had almost collided and both
drivers were livid with rage. Then one diplomatic passenger quickly rolled down his window, smiled at the
other driver, and said, "That was a close call, but we're
okay, I hope you are." The other driver gulped, nodded,
then smiled weakly, saying, "Yes, we're all right. No
harm done, I guess." And another argument was averted
through diplomacy.

16. *Apply logic and humor.* Calvin Coolidge, while Vice-
President and presiding officer of the Senate, was noted
for his calm and dry wit. One day when tempers flared,
one senator so far forgot himself as to bitterly denounce
a colleague, bidding him "go to hell." The maligned senator indignantly appealed to the chair, saying, "I've never
been so humiliated and insulted. I resent the senator's
demand that I go to hell, and I appeal to the chair for
relief." Coolidge paused for only a moment, then said,
"On the senator's appeal from the demand of his colleague that he go to hell—the chair rules that the maligned senator does not have to go." The entire Senate,
including the two feuding senators, joined in the hearty
laughter that cleared the atmosphere of much of this
moment of tension.

17. *Try prayer.* No man can pray for another and still

hate him, says Dr. William Barclay. The surest way of killing bitterness is to pray for the man we are tempted to hate. If the other fellow exasperates you, pray for your own composure—and for him. We are less likely to become angry at the person for whom we've just prayed.

Once known as "Terrible-Tempered" Tommy Bolt, the former U.S. Open golf champion would miss a putt, fly into a rage, and wrap his golf club around the nearest tree. The more he blew his top, the more the gallery would heckle and the more he'd miss an easy shot and display more temper. Tommy Bolt learned to control his temper through prayer. He says, "I reconditioned my attitudes. I put safety valves on my temper. I promised the Lord I would help Him help me. I strengthened my faith and put my trust in Someone bigger than I—and it worked."

"If religion has done nothing for your temper, it has done nothing for your soul," says James B. Clayton. And in the words of Saint Francis of Sales, "Every morning compose your soul for a tranquil day. Be not upset. Humble yourself before God and try to bring your mind into a quiet attitude. Be calm." To the extent that each of us follows these admonitions, we will better control our tempers and remove another tension roadblock and open the road to relaxation.

REJECT RESENTMENT

If you consider your mind to be a limitless and rich ore-bearing mine, a burst of anger is like a mine explosion. It is an emotional explosion that causes mental and emotional damage. There is no possible advantage to an angry outburst except that when it is over you are temporarily free of it and can begin repairing the damage. Resentment is closely allied to anger, but in many ways it is even worse. Unlike an anger explosion, resentment is a smoldering underground fire that does equal damage because, while lower in intensity, it is harder to root out. Resentment is a continuous stoking of smoldering tension fires that can burn out your emotional resources and keep the tension pot simmering. Here again the sensible solution is the right one. Instead of simply simmering resentfully, stop and examine the causes of your resentment. When you do, you will find in most cases that they are molehills that you have magnified into mountains.

If your resentment is directed against another person, bring it out into the open and, as fairly and reasonably as you can, discuss it with that person. In almost all cases you will find that an objective examination and discussion will clear up the tension-producing resentment that has been corroding your mind.

If the resentment is due to a situation rather than an individual, again put on your mental brakes. Look at the problem as objectively and as sensibly as you can. Define the problem to yourself, and make an ironclad decision to see what can be done about it. Then do it. God has given you the intelligence to think and to analyze any problem objectively—without resentment and without malice. Unless you are psychotic, you and you alone can best decide the solution to the problem. When you have decided the best possible approach, put it into action. Don't just allow it to continue without the attempt to improve or eliminate it.

If there is a problem to which you cannot find a solution, accept it. It may not be pleasant, but you will have to learn to live with it, and brooding resentfully will only make it that much worse.

DON'T CARRY A GRUDGE

A grudge is much too heavy a load for anyone small enough to carry it. Brooding over real or imagined hurts can become a chronic and destructive habit. Relaxation is impossible if you allow yourself to harbor a grudge against another. Stop and consider. Maybe your partner did double-cross you or give you a raw deal. Maybe Jack Henshaw did prevent you from making that deal or getting that raise, but to carry a grudge about it will hurt you more than it will hurt him. Remember that a grudge is due to something that has happened in the past and that the past is over. Look forward, not back. The same God who gave us the gift of memory so that we can recall the wonderful things that have happened also gave us forgetfulness. Remember the roses in December; forget the thorns.

Above all, wash your mind of the petty and destructive attitude of "getting even." To avenge a wrong is to get even with your adversary; to hate him is to fall beneath him; to forgive is to rise above him. Free your heart of bitterness and you will free yourself of a major source of tension. To forgive an enemy and, if you are big enough to do it, to love him, is a kind of exquisite common sense. It is enlightened self-interest. When you forgive someone you feel has done you a wrong, you are the one who has won the victory. You are the one who will have taken a long step to inner peace. So, be wise and selfish enough to forgive every man's faults except your own. The greatest teacher in the history of mankind taught us to be kind and to forgive one another.

DON'T BE A GROUCH

Any moron can easily fall into this destructive, ill-tempered habit. It's easy to begin, but it's difficult to end. Watch yourself. When you give a gruff and ill-tempered response, stop and listen to yourself. Then think of how you would react if you were on the receiving end. Grouchness is a matter of habit, the habit of reacting to any situation in an ill-tempered, sour way. It can sour your own attitudes and do you harm. No sensible person wants to spend time with a grouch. You are a sensible person, and if you allow yourself to fall into this habit, you will be forced to spend your whole life with one.

WATCH THESE TRAITS AND TENDENCIES:

1. *Don't be a nervous gabber.* Tension often makes people chatter incessantly and hog every conversation, so don't be a nervous gabber. As you become less tense, you will find this trait disappearing. Relax more and speak less. Speak less and relax more. Unless, of course, you have something to say. "It is better to keep the mouth closed and be thought a fool than to open it and remove all doubt." Patience and tongue control will noticeably lessen the tension of your listeners and of yourself.

2. *Don't carry a chip on your shoulder.* If someone makes a stupid or foolish statement, don't verbally jump

all over him. You will only create a tense situation when with a little diplomacy and a reasonable attitude you can eliminate it. "I never step aside for fools," said the man with a chip on his shoulder. "I do," said the diplomat, stepping aside to let him pass.

3. *Don't procrastinate in making decisions.* Indecision is a major trait that results in tension. Some people find that making even trivial decisions makes them tense and nervous, and yet we know that eventually decisions must be made. Procrastination only makes for more tension. Decide, and carry your decision out as soon as possible.

4. *Never second guess yourself.* After you have made your decision, carry it out as quickly as possible, and never look back. After you have acted, doubt and second-guessing may produce tension, but they will not produce a change in something that has already happened. Constantly looking back is useless and nonproductive. "If I had only . . . " is an utter waste of time and effort. Constantly looking back and castigating yourself provides an atmosphere that breeds needless tension and makes relaxation impossible. To relax you must make your decision, act on it, and then forget it. You did your best to do the right thing, and only a fool can be angry with someone who has done his best. Second-guessing one's self is one of the most vicious of all tension producers. Every time you start to look back and blame yourself, you are putting up a tension roadblock on the road to relaxation.

5. *Watch your sensitivity quotient.* Steer a course between the weakness of oversensitivity and the coldness of insensitivity. The oversensitive are obsessed with self, constantly conjuring up imaginary slights that cause needless emotional wounds and resentment, even toward

those closest to them. Use your intelligence. The world does not consist of people whose major preoccupation is to hurt your feelings or persecute you. The world consists of people just like you, who sometimes say or do thoughtless things that hurt. Don't let a chance remark, which you may have misunderstood, cause you needless pain.

The other side of the sensitivity coin is the insensitive egoist who is so concerned with himself that he has no respect for the sensitivity of others. The worst offenders are those combining extreme sensitivity toward themselves with hardness of head and heart to others. Let the Golden Rule guide you between these two tension-producing faults.

6. *Avoid blind prejudice.* A major tension trait is blind prejudice. It is to be found everywhere, always without logic and always producing inner tension. If you assume a dogmatic, prejudiced habit of thinking, you are putting needless shackles on your reasoning power and assuring yourself of needless tension. Prejudice simply means to prejudge an individual, a group, or a problem without examining the facts. Prejudice exists between races, between the sexes, between political powers, and between different economic groups. Almost everyone has some blind spot, some narrow-minded viewpoint that makes him a smaller, tenser, and less happy person than he should be.

There are blacks and whites, Catholics and Protestants, bosses and workers, who are equally prejudiced against each other. The Republican who assumes that every Democrat is socialistic and corrupt is as stupid as the Democrat who believes every Republican to be a tax-evading antilabor big-business tool. The black man who thinks that every white man is part of a conspiracy to exploit him and keep him down is just as mistaken as the white man who thinks every black male is a shiftless freeloader.

Every Democrat will encounter a Republican, and every white man will encounter a black man, in the course of his normal activities. If he prejudges any individual without evidence, he is breaking God's law and harming himself.

No man has a right to prejudice, but every man has a right to his preference. *Discrimination* is one of the most abused words in modern life. You have the right as well as the duty to discriminate between good and evil. You are entitled to seek out those whose characters and abilities you admire. It is your right to choose your friends and associates, the places you frequent, and where you want to live. But remember, you pay an exorbitant price for blind prejudice. Senseless hatred is a dubious luxury no one wishing to avoid tension can afford.

FRUSTRATION

Frustration induces a major portion of our tensions, and yet frustration of some kind has always been with us and will never be eliminated. It is a part of the human condition. It is the minor, often petty frustrations that too often defeat us. Frustration simply means not being able to have something you want, yet no one in the history of the world has ever had everything he desired.

There are two kinds of frustrations—those we can do something about, and those over which we have no control. The following situations are examples of the first type of frustration: When the morning of that long-awaited picnic begins with an all-day downpour, we feel frustrated. The solution is not to curse the weather in frustration, but to decide on an alternate indoor activity, which may be even more pleasurable. When an unexpected family illness destroys the nest egg you had earmarked for a European vacation, you can postpone and work for that dream until it becomes a reality.

Then there are frustrations of the second type—those over which we have no control. Yet with simple common sense and proper attitudes we can overcome these, too.

There are many conditions in modern life that lead to annoyance at best and despair at worst. To stretch the term, one could call one's attitude toward them *frustration*. There is a serious drug problem, dishonesty and hypocrisy in government, and a rising crime rate. The type of patriotism that our fathers believed in is now considered old-fashioned and even ridiculous. While the generation gap has always existed, there is an increasing lack of communication between young and old. The country has just ended an undeclared and unpopular war. Political morality continues to sink on all levels of government. While the great middle mass of taxpayers carry the heaviest burden and many of the wealthiest escape their fair share of taxation, the poorest are supported by the public purse. Crime in the streets is matched by a lack of integrity in public office. In a fundamentally biracial society, irresponsibility and racism on both sides have increased enormously. Even among the clergy there is confusion and lack of leadership. These are some of the darker aspects of American life that produce "frustration."

Instead of saying "What's the use?" each individual must do his best to help solve our national problems.

Resourceful men and women seek and find solutions instead of moaning about conditions. If you are unable to help find the solution to some problem, always remember that however grim things may look at any point in time, "this too shall pass."

4

You Are
Your Attitude

THE PROPER WAY TO START YOUR DAY

The noisy clang of our Big Ben sounding off at five o'clock, even on a cold, wintry morning, was the harshest, most unwelcome sound of my boyhood experience. That ungodly noise at our house meant hopping out onto an icy cold floor, leaping into cold clothes in an unheated room, and dashing downstairs to the living room chunk stove. It was always our hope to find a few dying embers that could be nursed into flame, with an additional log and wide-open damper in the stovepipe. Otherwise, two shivering preteen boys had a wood fire to build in a cold house.

Getting up under such circumstances was a rugged way to start the day. Yet we were taught to wake up cheerful and stay that way. We were challenged to meet the dawn head on, with heads up and a thankful heart. "Early to bed, early to rise" was drummed into us until we were obedient, if not entirely convinced. According to modern sophisticates, that philosophy is only for the birds, but those who don't follow it miss a lot, for early rising has its compensations. To watch the sun come up at dawn is a soul-stirring experience. And a little exercise in the early morning whets the appetite, causes the blood to course through your veins, and reminds you that it's good to be alive as you face a new day.

No matter what the method or starting time, it's important to start our day right. If we face each new day with pleasant thoughts and a zest for living, we're off to a good start. Most of us get up too late, with too little sleep, a sour stomach, and a surly disposition. Starting out with an I-hate-life outlook, we rush through our brief morning chores, gulp down a cup of coffee, then rush to meet deadlines as we fight traffc and tempers. We start the day under tension and pressure and grow more tense as normal daily pressures increase.

The solution is so simple that we ignore our own good judgment. Common sense tells us that all we need do is start off easy and relaxed. Then stay relaxed. To start out in a rush, full of tension and confusion, is to abandon your best hope for a relaxed day right at the start. Adopt the right attitude. Make your new year's resolution *now*. Start your new program tomorrow morning. This decision will bring you increased happiness and greater relaxation.

Here are suggested steps already known to most of us. Each will help. If taken together as a persistent daily diet, they unquestionably will help yourself and your associates to a more relaxed life.

Upon waking in the morning, look up first. "They that

seek the Lord shall not lack any good thing," wrote the Psalmist. Learn this truth and practice it all your days. Give thanks for the new day and the blessings you enjoy. At least send up a silent prayer of gratitude and appreciation. Be thankful to be alive. Face the new day with a feeling of anticipation and optimism. Send out thought waves of goodwill.

No man should get out of bed without first blessing himself and his neighbor. It may be little more than a deep-down feeling of head and heart, of appreciation, goodwill, and compassion for mankind and a soul in harmony with the Creator of the universe.

After your meditation, remain in relaxed stillness for a while, listening for God's guidance, inspiration, and comfort. Face the new day with calmness, serenity, and peace. Resolve to let your mind, spirit, and body go with God.

Seriously try this rule. Deliberately practice it each morning as you awake. You'll soon find this approach to each new day coming in a flash to your subconscious mind, even before you open your eyes. A heart full of love is more than mere emotion and sentiment. Blessing others and being thankful for your own blessings develop that "it's good to be alive" feeling and attitude. This is the real secret of how to start your day right. Follow this rule and you can forgo the other steps.

Shake yourself awake. Stretch, yawn, and take a few deep breaths of fresh air. Open your eyes and, lying on your back, hands cupped under your head and feet stretched well down toward the foot of the bed, breathe deeply, draw your stomach high up under your ribs, and yawn and stretch repeatedly. By now you should at least be conscious of the new day. Take a tip from your dog.

Notice how he stretches, yawns, and exercises after a long nap.

Now, awake and in the proper frame of mind, get going. Jump out! Don't creep or crawl. Get up—on the double—awake in body, mind, and spirit. Come alive, ready for the day ahead. Then, jump into the tub or shower. Give yourself a brisk rubdown. At the very least splash cold water on your face, eyes, and neck. Massage well behind your ears, rolling your eyes in a brisk rotary motion. Then with wet fingertips massage your scalp well before combing or brushing your hair. By this time you should be thoroughly awake. Your eyes will be open, the blood will be circulating to your head, and you'll feel and look awake.

To wake up inside, get the water-drinking habit. Drink a full glass of water before retiring and another as soon as you're up in the morning. The water will gently massage you inside while you sleep and as you take your morning exercise. Be sure to exercise, using whatever calisthenics you find helpful. They need not be strenuous, but take some regular exercise before dressing for the day.

Shave promptly, or apply your makeup, as the case may be. Put your best face forward. Take time to shave, or to make up, even on your day off. Just seeing the instant improvement in the mirror will help your disposition. Smiling, whistling, humming, or singing as you shave or put on makeup helps you start the day with the corners of your mouth turned up. Try it. You'll feel better. If you'll start the day with a song on your lips and in your heart, you'll look better to others and to yourself.

Eat a good breakfast. Morning is the time your body needs the nourishment necessary to fortify itself for another grueling day, but 50 percent of our urban population goes to work on an empty stomach. If you don't drag your body to work without proper nourishment, it's less likely to drag you down later in the day.

Polish up your breakfast manners. Don't greet your family with a growl. Grouchiness is contagious, especially in the morning. Cheerfulness is good for your health and it's a tonic for the mind and body. It has a direct, beneficial influence upon the nerves and internal organs. It is a medicial fact that cheerful people resist disease better. As one doctor puts it, "It's the surly bird that catches the germ." Cheerfulness is a valuable business and social asset. It is the antidote to worry, fear, and discord. Cheerfulness leads to alertness, serenity, and vigor. Stay cheerful and you'll stay relaxed. Be a boy scout. Pause long enough to do at least one kind act, one good turn, for someone who needs a lift. One good boy scout act each day will enrich many lives, including your own.

Exude goodwill as you go. Have a pleasant greeting for your neighbor, the bus operator, or the parking lot attendant. Speak to the janitor and elevator operator and watch them perk up. Try to give your fellow workers' spirits a lift with a cheerful greeting or some little pleasantry. Cheerfulness, courtesy, and happiness are just as contagious as the measles, and lots more fun. You can't sprinkle sunshine without some of it falling on you. Try to live each day as though it were your last day on earth, and treat everyone you meet as though it were his last day and only you knew it.

Take it easy. Don't rush around propelled by anxieties and nervousness. "Sufficient unto the day is the evil thereof." Live one day at a time. Take time to be pleasant, patient, courteous, and considerate of others and you'll discover that you have more time left for relaxed use in fruitful channels of your own seeking.

You can start each new day right and stay relaxed through the day, if you really want to. If you'll practice these rules, in spite of everything and everybody that get in the way, they'll soon pay off. You may feel awkward and foolish at first, but they'll get easier with practice. You may be the subject of some ridicule, but you'll also be the subject of satisfying rewards.

Make your new year's resolution now! Observe these rules tomorrow morning and never stop. Pursue this course relentlessly and life will be more meaningful, pleasant and more relaxed. "With every rising of the sun, think of your life as just begun." Start your day on a cheerful note that is planned and charted and you can stay cheerful for the balance of the day. Keep it up until it becomes habitual, and you'll live a happier, healthier, and more relaxed life. You may even live longer.

SMILE AT OTHERS AND YOU CAN LAUGH AT TROUBLE

A smile costs nothing. It happens in a flash and is gone. But the memory can last forever. A smile has the therapeutic effect of unlocking tense muscles. A smile and worry won't mix. A smile should be the first thing a successful person dons each morning and the last thing he removes at night. It takes only thirteen muscles to smile and requires sixty-four muscles to frown. Every time you frown, you vaccinate yourself against happiness. Of all the things you wear, your expression is the most important. Keep a smile on your face, or at least keep one in nearby reserve.

A smiling countenance opens many doors. "Smile if you plan to enroll," was the closing appeal of one highly successful Dale Carnegie promoter, at the climax of his public sales presentation. Then, he'd pause, smile at the audience, and say, "In fact, smile anyway—at least, don't frown. You're our guest. If you haven't decided to enroll tonight, then we wouldn't want you to do so. Don't be uncomfortable. You're among friends. Sit back and relax while others enroll. We're glad you came and want you to be also." This approach, accompanied by a grin, seemed to melt opposition and put both the sold and unsold at ease. I suspect that this low-pressure approach sold more undecided enrollees than any high-pressure closing tactics he could have devised.

There is no weapon in the whole feminine armory to which men are so vulnerable as the smile. There is nothing like the lure of a genuine smile to get a man's attention and cause him to want to see more of you.

Can you act cheerful and gay when you don't feel that way? Can a man always substitute a smile and a pleasant greeting for that dark-brown mental taste and grouchy feeling? Despite all the propaganda to the contrary, the customer isn't always right. In fact, more frequently, when he insists upon his rights, he's dead wrong. That's why one fed-up salesman joined the police force—he wanted a job where the customer was always wrong.

Even if you can't smile, at least don't snarl, sneer, or "snile." Showing the teeth, without the sincerity and warmth that spring only from the heart, is only a snile or smirk that sickens the beholder and exposes the wearer as a fake.

Of course we must be realistic. Life is full of rough spots. Each man has his share of problems, disappointments, and disillusionments. Can a rational person really be expected to smile on the outside when he's crying on the inside? It isn't easy, but you'll accomplish it more often with conscious effort. It takes the right attitude, backed up by common sense and determination.

A smile makes sense. I don't expect you to smile when you break your leg or lose your life's savings, but an inner and outer smile helps cushion the unpleasant shocks of life. Remind yourself constantly to smile, to think of the pleasant instead of the unpleasant aspects of each day. It's a mental habit, and when you have formed it you will radiate sunshine, automatically. Some of it will bounce back on you.

LAUGHTER IS TENSION MEDICINE

Frank Bettger once told a large Washington audience, "I was an utter failure and the worst sourpuss in the world until I learned to laugh." He had evidently learned, for he drew $500, or $25 per minute, for that humorous twenty-minute talk. For thirty years Frank Bettger was one of the highest-paid insurance salesmen in the nation, largely because of his sense of humor. Frank not only could laugh, he could laugh at himself.

Joe E. Brown became wealthy by converting a long, serious face into his infectious ear-to-ear grin.

J. E. McKerracher during the merger of nine companies, was called into New York with other division heads scheduled to be lopped off. But Mack refused to worry. Instead of being fired, he was given a better job, largely because of his ability to laugh at trouble.

Boarding the crowded elevator that morning for the

executive offices of Remington Rand, McKerracher explained to the operator why the faces of so many passengers had that strained and worried look. Then taking out a new one-dollar bill, in mock seriousness, Mack hired the elevator operator to do all his worrying for him for that day.

Before they reached the twentieth floor, everybody was enjoying the fun, including the new president, who, unknown to the group, was also a passenger. It was his later decision that the company could not afford to lose a man with such a cheerful disposition and keen sense of humor. So McKerracher returned to the field in a position of greater authority.

Jim Hurt, vice-president of Culpeper Stone Company, was under medical treatment for ulcers when this author spoke before his Rotary Club in 1958. Jim later joined a Carnegie class, regained his natural personality and delightful sense of humor, and soon had no ulcers, no worries, and no need for medication. He learned to laugh at problems. He refused to worry and learned to relax.

Laughter pays off. The more you laugh, and the easier it is for you to laugh, the healthier you'll be. You can't grow ulcers while you laugh. If you want to relax, join the gloom chasers and laugh. It's good for you and a tonic to others. When you share a sorrow, you divide it, but when you share a joy, you multiply it. It is still true that if you laugh, the world laughs with you. Weep, and you weep alone.

Why not try clown "Pappy" Dan Kerr's daily prayer? "Lord help me create more laughter than tears, dispense more happiness than gloom, and spread more cheer than despair. Help me make people laugh and forget, momentarily at least, all the unpleasant things in their lives."

Learn to see the funny side of life. A sense of humor can be cultivated. And a good start is to learn to laugh at yourself. The man who can laugh at his own stupid mistakes and misfortunes is not a jackass. It hurts less if you have the horse sense to laugh.

Dale Carnegie always kept by his desk what he called his D.F.M. file, for his mistakes. "Bill," he told me, "I try not to make too many mistakes. But when I do make one, it is a beauty. If it is in writing, I always file the blooper in my 'darn fool mistake' file. Then when I find myself feeling smug and self-satisfied, I reach for my D.F.M. file and read about some of my asinine mistakes. It always helps me to laugh at myself."

Repeat good jokes that tickle your funny bone. The chances are that others will enjoy them also. And don't apologize, ever, for a talk or a joke that someone may have heard before. If it isn't worth hearing a second time, then it probably wasn't worth telling in the first place. Here are true stories of humorous incidents that actually happened.

This author's wife was president of the Women's Missionary Society of Calvary Baptist Church in Washington, D.C., for three years. The good ladies had invited her husband and her pastor to sit at the head table and speak at the testimonial dinner given for retiring officers. Acting as chairman, the judge's wife apparently was a bit nervous. When she rose to introduce me, she said, "For three years we have listened with delight to our president. Now you'll have to listen to Ruby's wife, Bill."

The chairman became flustered and nervous. But, sensing her embarrassment, her pastor came to the rescue. "Don't let that little bobble throw you, Madame Chairman," he said. "Why only recently I was attending a reception for retiring General George C. Marshall when Ambassador Grew made a similar slip of the tongue. The ambassador had been most generous in his praise of the general when he paused and said, 'But I'm sure that General Marshall doesn't want me to continue to outline his many well-known accomplishments. In fact, I happen to know, ladies and gentlemen, that all General Marshall wants to do is to settle down, quietly, in Leesburg, Virginia, and spend the balance of his life with Mrs. Eisenhower.' "

My wife and I were married in Nashville, Tennessee. A few hours later we boarded the L&N for our honeymoon in the East. When the porter had brushed off the rice and ushered us into our drawing room, I gave him a five-dollar bill, telling him we didn't want anyone to know that we were newlyweds. Palming the five-spot, he readily agreed to keep our secret. But the next morning as we returned from the diner, everyone in the coach stared and smiled at us, to my bride's embarrassment.

Indignant, I rang for the porter and, after dressing him down for telling, demanded the return of my five dollars. "I didn't tell, honest I didn't. Why, when you came out of your bedroom on your way to breakfast, a man in the back of the coach asked if you wasn't just married, and I told him, 'No, they're not married, they're just good friends.' "

The new father of triplets had a six-year-old son who had been praying for months for a baby brother, but finally became discouraged and quit. Later the father took the lad by the hospital to see his mother and stopped at the nursery. Pointing out the three babies, he said, "See there, son, aren't you glad you prayed for a little brother?" "Yep," said the lad, "and, Dad, aren't you glad I stopped praying when I did?"

Back in the do-it-yourself booze era of Prohibition, one batch of home brew turned out unusually well. Everybody wanted the recipe, but the maker couldn't remember what ingredients he had used. On the advice of friends, he sent a gallon of the liquid to a chemist for analysis, without an identifying label. A few days later he received the chemist's report, which read: "Dear Sir— We have diligently analyzed the liquid specimen you forwarded to us, and while our findings are by no means conclusive, it is our considered judgment that your horse has sugar diabetes."

Laughter is the sensation of feeling good all over and showing it in principally one spot. Learn to laugh. For he who laughs—lasts.

WHISTLE WHILE YOU WORK—OR PLAY

You can't be mean while you're whistling. Can you imagine Stalin or Hitler whistling? Whistling is good for your lungs, according to Dr. Maurice S. Segal, professor at Tufts University Medical School in Boston. Dr. Segal claims that whistling "can aid chronic lung ailment by widening constricted breathing tubes in the body, relieving shortness of breath." So, whistle while you work and play—the lung you save may be your own.

My elderly neighbor Harold Stabler was a celebrated bird watcher. He fed and watered a host of birds all winter in his bird sanctuary. I'm indebted to this distinguished octogenarian for his bird friends we both enjoyed. During the past summer, a Stabler-sponsored mockingbird put on·an early morning recital just outside my bedroom window. Often during the day, without the slightest hesitation or fear, that bird would appear in a pine tree and sing to us as we drove off in the car. Sometimes, when we were working in the rear yard, he'd fly to a nearby limb and literally whistle at us. Sometimes I wonder if God in His infinite wisdom didn't put a song in the throat of a bird as a reminder to man that this universe was meant to be a happy, cheerful place.

Whistling unquestionably is good for you. So whistle while you work and as you play. It's a morale builder. Whistling may not make your load any easier, but it will make it seem lighter.

As a salesman I used to make a game of what you might call harmony-priming. I'd get into a cab whistling and soon even the grouchy driver would join. Or I'd whistle as I entered a building or office and I found that ears and doors opened more readily. Try it. Whistle as you walk up any street of any town. You'll find that strangers will smile and sometimes speak to you. If they don't know you, they'll want to get acquainted.

A cheerful whistle is one of nature's best ways to make friends. It opens doors and hearts. Try it and you'll find that the world welcomes a whistler. If you'd like to relax— if you'd like to see others relax—whistle and watch people whistle along in harmony.

SING YOUR WORRIES AWAY

Most people love music. And, blessed with a good baritone voice, in his youth this writer made some. Throat cancer silenced my singing voice years ago. Today I sing on the inside, in gratitude for partial restoration. One has only to lose his voice and find it again to appreciate its true worth. No matter what happens, I shall try never to lose the song in my heart, for without inner harmony man is a poor creature indeed.

Most men sing, many as they shower and shave. Some sing in the rain or in the dark. They often sing as they work. All God's creatures seem to be members of a universal choir. By nature we're all singers. And since a good way for a human being to relax is for him to make music, why not get in tune with the universe and sing?

To live with life's problems, keep a song often on your lips and constantly in your heart. Singing and tensions don't mix. If you can't sing the scale, you can at least listen. Cultivate appreciation for laughter and music. If you can't sing—listen. Listen as the birds burst into song with each new day. Learn from them. If it's natural for a bird to sing, think how much more natural and logical it should be for man's spirit to burst forth in song. If you can't sing, even if you can no longer hear, listen to your heart and sing inside.

There's music everywhere about you, even on the written page. Feast your eyes and spirit on cheerful vibrations. Memorize and repeat the words of some of your favorite hymns and songs. They can insulate you against tension in time of trouble. Here are some lines from

"God Will Take Care of You," the writer's favorite cushion:

> Be not dismayed, whate'er betide, God will take
> care of you
> Beneath his wings of love abide, God will take care
> of you
> Thru every day, o'er all the way; He will take care
> of you.

Smile when you can, and laugh at life when you can't. Hum a bit now and then, and whistle often. But sing from morning till night. Sing your blues away—and relax.

THE THERAPY OF TEARS

"There is a time to weep and a time to laugh," says the Book of Books. Great men of every age both prayed and wept. During the darkest days of World War II, Sir Winston Churchill often burst into tears. Yet he was not weak. George Washington wept at Valley Forge. Lee wept over the plight of his defeated Confederate army. Lincoln wept over a nation under God, half slave and half free, with each side breeding bitterness and hatred toward the other.

Men do not usually brag about a trait that their fellows consider to be a weakness. Tears are sometimes an indication of humility, of humaneness, empathy, understanding, and compassion. And often joy.

Is there a therapeutic value in your tears and mine? Tears are the floodgates that open to relieve unbearable tension pressures. Tears are safety values of the heart when too much pressure is laid upon it. If God gave man a smile for a purpose, surely He had in mind some good purpose for a tear. Why not turn loose your tears and relax?

Tears are a natural emotional outlet; they drain off tension and leave man with a more relaxed personality. Tears are safety valves that sometimes explode in a burst of anger, and subside in contrition, tenderness, and forgiveness. The individual who, because of the hardness of his heart, can no longer cry, no longer shed a tear, has strangled his heart and deadened his sensitivity.

No man should ever grow too big or too old to shed a tear. Tears are the most relaxing therapy known to man. Don't deny yourself the rich experience of a tear-moist eye and heart. Don't ever forget how to weep. Man is the only animal tha. cries. God planned it that way. "Blessed are you that weep now," Jesus said, "for you shall laugh."

ACCENTUATE THE POSITIVE

Gloomy Gus was not his name, but that is what we called him, behind his back and sometimes to his face. "GG" was pessimism personified, a disciple of perpetual gloom. GG was a pessimist who liked to listen to the patter of little defeats. To be around GG was terribly depressing. He was a defeatist. Everything was wrong. The whole world was bad and getting worse. GG always felt unjustly abused, maligned, and unlucky. He was full of self-pity, bitterness, and resentment.

To GG everything was the darkest shade of black. There was no white or gray. GG looked at a bleak world through dark glasses. Each morning he arrived at the office in a gloomy mood to match his black hat, black tie, and black suit. He seldom arrived without his black umbrella, for he constantly expected it to rain all over him. He had the whole wide world on his back, couldn't forget it, and wouldn't let you forget it either.

Why do people like Gus always look for the worst? Why do they forget that we can only go into the woods halfway, and the rest of the time we're coming out?

The darkest hour is only sixty minutes long. It, too, will pass. Why constantly anticipate the worst, unless the worst is what you really want? If you go through life expecting to fail, you're almost sure to fail. When you bog down in the quicksands of pessimism, you've already started to sink. Think constantly of illness and you make yourself sick.

Why settle for less than the best? You deserve the best, and you're more likely to get it if you expect and work for it. The best is none too good for the man who walks on the sunny side of the street with an optimistic outlook. A cheerful, optimistic disposition is more precious than rubies. The person who always travels in an atmosphere of optimism will never be too unlucky, too unhappy, or too lonesome.

Victor Hugo said, "An optimist is like a bird perched on a frail bough, who feels the branch give way, yet keeps on singing for it knows it has wings for flight." Optimism is faith in action. Life does not always consist in holding a good hand, but in playing a bad hand well. Optimism is doing the best you can with what you have. Optimism is expecting clear skies but being prepared to weather any storm.

If fate throws a dagger your way, there are two places to take hold of it—by the blade or by the handle. Grab the blade and you're apt to get cut. Grasp it by the handle and you can make it do your bidding. When you get to the end of your rope, tie a knot in it and hang on. That's optimism.

The only difference between an optimist and a pessimist is, the optimist laughs to forget while the pessimist forgets to laugh. If it weren't for the optimist, the pessimist wouldn't even know how happy he wasn't. A pessimist generally has too much jawbone and not enough backbone.

If you can't be an optimist, don't be a cynic or pessimist. Don't go through life in reverse. Negative thinking produces negative results. If you sow fear germs, expect a crop of failures. If you send out powerful goodwill vibrations of health and happiness, they are more likely to come your way. "As a man thinketh in his heart so is he" (Proverbs 5:23:1) and so, frequently, is his neighbor.

Here are guidelines to help you steer clear of pessimism and detour around the slough of despond:

1. *Don't second-guess yourself.* Indecision is the most negative, insidious, and deadly character trait. Once having made a decision, put the matter from your mind. Nothing will make you more jittery, irritable, and unhappy than constantly rehashing decisions and changing your mind over what has been done. It never pays to cry over spilled milk. Consider the facts. Make your decision and forget it. Live one day at a time and don't anticipate tomorrow's troubles. Don't be a floogie bird, which flies backward because it doesn't care where it's going but only wants to see where it's been. Obstacles are those hazards we see when we take our eyes off the goal.

2. *Don't be a crepe hanger.* Life is sometimes unfair and confusing. It doesn't make sense for Swiss cheese to

have all those holes, when it's Limburger that really needs the ventilation, but don't let that make you sour on life.

The prankster rubbed Limburger cheese thoroughly into the moustache of the drunk asleep on the barroom floor. When the drunk awoke, he raised his head, sniffed a few times, struggled to his feet, and staggered into the street. He faced up the street and smelled, then faced down the street and took a good smell, shook his head in disgust and muttered, "The whole world stinks."

3. *Don't complain.* When feeling out of sorts, don't complain to others. To complain is a telltale sign of a guilt feeling. Do what you think is right. "When you are in the right," said Gandhi, "you can afford to keep your composure, and when you're in the wrong you can't afford to lose it."

4. *Don't blame others to excuse yourself.* It has always been man's tendency to shift the blame to his neighbor. Out of feelings of guilt or inferiority, some people blame others for their every misfortune. They need a whipping boy or scapegoat. They rationalize the fault or shift the blame elsewhere.

According to a modern version, Adam and his son were out strolling and happened to pass by the Garden of Eden. The boy stared, then turning to his father said, "Say, that's a swell place; why don't we live there?" "We did," Adam replied sadly, "until your mother ate us out of house and home."

5. *Don't bore others with your troubles.* People who enjoy telling about their bad luck or poor health not only bore their listeners, but greatly increase their own susceptibility to further ills. Telling your troubles only swells them.

Up to his neck in economic and political trouble, out of a job and in poor health, my friend ex-congressman Brooks Hays was asked, "How do you feel?" I shall never forget the pathetic, sickly look on his face as he replied, "Bill, I feel just terrible. If you've got thirty minutes to spare, I'd like to tell you about it." He was dead serious, but only for a moment. Then forcing a great big smile he said, "I'm joking; I've felt better than I do today, but it'll pass. I'll feel better tomorrow. In fact, I feel better already. Thanks for asking."

That quick recovery and response required intelligence. It took character to reverse himself so readily. He was no bore. His was the courageous spirit that travels in an atmosphere of optimism. Shortly thereafter he became assistant to the President of the United States. All of us could learn much from the attitude of this ex-congressman.

6. *Don't indulge in self-pity.* Feeling sorry is the only thing that some people do for themselves, and even then they like help with it. It's a mistake to compare our lot with that of others and then conclude that we have not received fair consideration. The moment you start feeling sorry for yourself, you're on the tension toboggan. Sit down for a moment, think, and relax. Cast off your problems as you would remove your sandals and shake out the sand.

Reject the negative in your thinking. Optimism isn't a surface bubble, but a deep well of inward peace and contentment, which all the tensions and all the ups and downs in life fail to disturb. Why not live in an atmosphere of optimism? Send out powerful goodwill vibrations. A cheerful, happy person is like a ray of sunshine to every life that crosses his path. Travel life's road with optimism. It's just as easy as walking in the gloom.

WORK IS TENSION THERAPY

To love your work is to make it play, rather than labor; joy instead of drudgery. It's important to your health, happiness, and success that you choose which approach you want to be your life's pattern.

"I never worked a day in my life. It was all play because I loved my work," said Thomas A. Edison. "Work is a cure for worry. I have a zest to press on, explore, discover, prove, and perfect."

"I believe in hard work," said Charles Evans Hughes. "Men do not break down from overwork, but from worry and dissipation." Work is as much a necessity to man as eating and sleeping.

Most people aren't lazy. Most people want to be helpful. Almost anybody will agree to help move the piano. The only trouble is that most of them want to carry the stool. The greatest failures are those who have the ability but lack the ambition to follow through. They know how, but due either to procrastination or indifference, they forgo the joy and dignity of orderly execution. Excellence in aptitude can be jeopardized by a senseless work attitude.

Carlyle wrote, "The most unhappy of all men is the man who has no work cut out for him. In idleness is perpetual despair. Work is the grand cure of all maladies and miseries that ever beset mankind—honest work which you intend getting done."

There are three kinds of labor. First is slave labor— tedious toil without pay. The second may be distasteful—

work for wages only, with little or no interest beyond the money. The third is the labor of love—directed toward service to others. It may be tedious to toil for wages, but it never can be wholly distasteful or unpleasant, if you have an eagerness and passion to do it, regardless of reward or compensation. Too many people live only to retire to a life of ease and inactivity. They impatiently await the day when their social security or retirement benefits become effective. They mentally build up a future utopia, but forget to live and work in the present. According to studies by the New York Life Insurance Company, men who suddenly and completely retire don't live long. It's too great a shock. They're not prepared for leisure. People live longer if they have a zest for living, for work and activity that keep them young. You will never really be old if you never really retire.

If and when you give up your business, be sure to take on a new interest. Keep active and busy, and enjoy life while you're able. You'll never know how much you'll miss your work until it's too late. Think of the person who said, "I grumbled because I had to get up in the morning, until one morning, when I couldn't get up."

Tune in on joy. Convert work from drudgery to play. Enter the contest with the sheer desire to enjoy. Lose track of reward or potential loss, and concentrate on what you believe. "If you can't work with love and joy, but only with distaste, it is better that you should leave your work and sit at the gate of the temple and ask alms of those who work with joy," said the late Edward R. Murrow.

Congressman Walter H. Judd of Minnesota was once asked where he got the energy to carry on his heavy work schedule in Congress and out, and replied, "I have one basic rule of living: Do the best you can and leave the rest to God! I believe in what I'm doing and then I do only what I believe. Consequently, I have the time of my life and my energy never seems to run down."

Thank God each morning when you get up that you have something to do that day that must be done. To do your best at work will breed in you temperance and self-control, diligence and strength of will, cheerfulness and contentment, and a hundred virtues the idle never know. Time does not hang heavy on the hands of a busy person. He's always active. If you want to be sure that something will be done on schedule, look up a busy man.

Hard work does not tear us down. The reverse is true. Hard work is a tonic for the human body. It's the strain and pressure under which we work that throw us. It's the hurried, confused pace in which we live that affects our health. A busy but relaxed, restful type of person is almost always healthy. To be relaxed is to face life's work with a calm and confident outlook that not only brings peace, deep down, but which radiates peace and goodwill toward men everywhere.

COAST THROUGH THE DAY IF YOU PLAN IT THAT WAY

If relaxation means absence of tension, why don't intelligent human beings avoid doing those things they know will make them tense? Why get into a dither each morning and stay there all day? Plan your day, then operate that way. Don't burn out your gears going up one side of unnecessary mountains, then burn up your brakes fighting the curves and steep grades going down the other side. Skirt the mountain entirely, with its boulders, cliffs, and precipices. Travel the freeway, use less fuel, and reduce travel time and distance.

Here are steps that will help prevent unnecessary friction in your daily routine. They are simple and obvious, but few of us, including the writer, have the good judgment always to observe them.

1. *Get up on time.* A typical day of the average man is one of rush, noise, and confusion. Why complicate matters further by starting late? Why dash into a day of inevitable turmoil bcause you started off on the wrong foot? Set a schedule that will allow you to bathe, shave, dress, eat, and travel leisurely to the day's challenges ahead.

2. *Relax en route.* If you drive to work, drive carefully. Sit behind the wheel in a comfortable position. Get into your lane and stay there. If some wild-eyed, half-awake nitwit cuts in, don't blow your top after you blow your horn. Let him race on. It may be that he's so often late he's now about to be fired. Or he may be a doctor, priest, or rabbi rushing to the bedside of some unfortunate who was in too big a hurry.

Don't chafe at the bit when traffic stops at a red light. This is your opportunity to notice the troubled or happy faces of others who daily join the mad race downtown. Take it easy. It's ten to one you'll get there safely and probably ahead of the fellow who constantly cuts in and out of line.

3. *Spread cheer as you go.* Say a cheery hello to the attendant who parks your car. Notice how his face lights up. Notice how much more quickly he brings your car in the evening. Speak to the traffic cop on the corner. He's human, too. He'll appreciate a civil word for a change.

4. *Start your day in comfort.* Make sure you work with proper ventilation and light. Nothing will make you tense and tired sooner than a stuffy, poorly ventilated room. Poor lighting not only causes eyestrain but breeds gloom in the room. A comfortable chair, properly adjusted for your workbench or desk, becomes increasingly important as the day wears on your nerves. The longer you retain an awkward, uncomfortable position, the more tension and strain you develop.

5. *Pause at noon.* Take three minutes to rest and relax before you go out to lunch. Wash up, remove your coat, loosen your tie and shoes, and stretch out on the flat of your back on a couch, if possible. If not, seated at your desk, rest your head and arms with your eyes closed. Or sit in a comfortable chair with palms resting on your lap, eyes closed. Breathe deeply and remain silent, relaxed, and motionless for three minutes. Breathe a silent prayer of grateful appreciation for your many blessings. Send out heartfelt goodwill and blessings toward mankind in general, and your associates in particular. Especially the one who irks you most.

6. *Relax while waiting.* Don't fret yourself into a bad humor because of unforeseen delays. Use your waiting time to review the subject matter of your meeting. Or read. Better still, sit quietly and loosely, resting your arms on the chair or with your palms down on your lap. Relax and rest until it's time for your meeting.

7. *Relax while listening.* At a stuffy conference or long-winded lecture at which your ears and brain rebel, at least be physically comfortable. Keep an open mind. Take notes. It will keep you occupied. And besides, you can throw them away later.

8. *Pause before starting home.* Take three minutes to

relax at the close of the day's labors before starting home. Use the noontime formula. You'll find that the evening traffic won't aggravate you nearly so much. And you'll arrive home in a much happier frame of mind.

9. *Vacation often.* Don't just take an annual vacation. Take vacations monthly, weekly, and daily. Snatch as many three-minute relaxing vacations as possible, each day.

10. *Take off your false face at dinner.* Share your good experiences of the day with the family. Don't dwell on the unpleasant ones. And don't depend on a false stimulant to pep you up.

11. *Enjoy your leisure.* Relax at home or with friends. Treat each evening as a vacation from duty, cares, and problems. Forget the cares of the day. Have fun, read, simmer down, and relax.

12. *Rest and sleep.* Sleep is the relaxation of over four hundred muscles. Once upon the mattress, remember that the bed is the place for refreshment, rest, and sleep. It is not a battleground for rehashing and refighting the lost skirmishes of the day. Neither is it a place to review secret animosities and irritations. As you lay aside your clothes, put aside the load from your mind and lie down to relax, rest, and sleep.

But no one should ever close his eyes for the night without first saying good night to his family and then to his Maker. After everything else is quiet, wait until all the little noises within you are still. Then pray. Pray to God in heaven—if you believe there is a god in heaven. Pray, "Thank you, Lord, for the blessings of this day. And bless mankind everywhere. And please, God, send me out tomorrow to help you do it!"

TAKE TIME TO LIVE

Only one minute separates life from death. Only one minute separates sunrise from sunset. It's morning until twelve noon, then in one minute we're headed toward evening. "One minute that has only sixty seconds in it. Forced upon me—can't refuse it. Didn't seek it, didn't choose it. I must suffer—if I lose it. Give account if I abuse it. Just a tiny little minute. But eternity is in it."

Man is the only creature on earth that time irritates. He alone carries a watch or watches a clock. Yet, he alone refuses to take time to relax and really live. Our very choice of words indicates the pell-mell rush in which we live each day. We jump out of bed, grab a bite, hop in the car, dash downtown, rush around all day, run a few errands, scurry home, and dress quickly in order to step out. Little wonder that doctors urge people to slow down and relax more. Ulcers are a by-product of our civilization. Ulcers are not found among primitive peoples, because they do not hurry their lives away.

"One of the most tragic things I know about human nature," Dale Carnegie once said, "is that all of us tend to put off living. We're all dreaming of some magical rose garden over the distant horizon of tomorrow, instead of enjoying the roses that are blooming outside our windows today." Meanwhile, time marches on. When you're a child, time creeps. When you're a youth, it lags. When you're a man, it runs. And when you are old, it's too soon gone.

We're in a whirl between sunrise and sunset. We're constantly admonished to take advantage of every moment, to make better use of our time, not to waste a minute. We're challenged to do it now—start at once. We're reminded that a journey of a thousand miles begins with a single step, and we're urged to take that first step *now*, and keep on stepping to get ahead. Yet, in the same breath, we're cautioned and advised to slow down, relax, take it easy, take time to live. It's a confusing paradox that adds to our tensions.

In the Good Book we're told, "To every thing there is a season, and a time to every purpose under the heaven. A time to be born and a time to die . . . a time to weep and a time to laugh . . . a time to keep silence and a time to speak."

In his credo, *Take Time To Live a Full Life*, General Douglas MacArthur said:

"Young" is not a time of life. It's a state of mind. It's a temper of the will, a quality of the imagination, a vigor of the emotions, a predominance of courage over timidity, of the appetite for adventure over love of ease.

Nobody grows old by merely living a number of years. People grow old only by deserting their ideals. Years wrinkle the skin, but to give up wrinkles the soul.

You are as young as your faith, as old as your doubt; as young as your self-confidence, as old as your fear; as young as your hope, as old as your despair.

So long as your heart receives messages of beauty, cheer, courage, grandeur and power from the earth, from man and from the Infinite, so long are you young.

When the wires are down, and all the central places of your heart are covered with the snows of pessimism and the ice of cynicism; then, and only then, are you grown old indeed, and may God have mercy on your soul.

You don't have to be an alcoholic to appreciate the wonderful philosophy of Alcoholics Anonymous, in this amended version of "Just for Today":

1. Just for today, I will try to live through this day only, and not tackle my whole life problem at once.

2. Just for today, I wil be happy by giving happiness to others, for happiness is from within.

3. Just for today, I will adjust myself to what is, and not try to adjust everything to my desires. I will take my "luck" as it comes; and fit myself to it.

4. Just for today, I will take care of my body. I will exercise it, care for it, nourish it, not abuse nor neglect it, so that it will be a perfect machine for my bidding.

5. Just for today, I will try to strengthen my mind. I wil study. I will learn something useful. I will not be a mental loafer. I will read something that requires effort, thought, and concentration.

6. Just for today, I will exercise my soul in three ways: I will do somebody a good turn, and not get found out. I will do at least two things I don't want to do, just for exercise. I will not allow anyone to hurt my feelings.

7. Just for today, I will be agreeable. I will look as well as I can, dress becomingly, talk low and courteously, criticize not one bit, not find fault with anything, and not try to improve or regulate anybody, except myself.

8. Just for today, I will have a quiet half hour all by myself and relax.

9. Just for today, I will have a program. I may not follow it exactly, but I will have it. I will save myself from two pests: hurry and indecision.

10. Just for today, I will be unafraid. Especially, I will not be afraid to enjoy what is beautiful, and to believe that as I give to the world, so the world will give to me.

Take time to live. Remember as we travel down life's highway that not every detour is unpleasant or without its compensations. Some of life's most irksome detours often prove to be life's most scenic highways, if only we take time to live as we travel along.

5

Look Out
and Look Up

LISTEN TO YOUR HEART

Man is fearfully and wonderfully made. He is a conglomerate consisting of infinitely more than mere animal matter. He is unique among all creatures, for man consists of body, mind, and spirit. Man was created in the image of God, but a little lower than the angels of heaven, and was given dominion over all the earth.

God gave to man a brain, so that he might reason and think; be capable of distinguishing right from wrong. He gave to man a heart, so that he might feel emotion and have compassion for all God's creatures. He gave man a spirit, so that he might rise above time and petty circumstance, and enjoy communion with his Maker. God gave man two legs so that he might stand upright, tall and straight, with head erect and shoulders square, and eyes to look the whole world in the face. God gave man a backbone, with enough flexibility that he might reach down a helping hand to lift a fallen brother, or raise his head to heaven as he gives grateful appreciation to the Father for his many blessings.

God did more. He created in the mind and heart of man His own image. He put something of Himself deep within the soul of man. He put His own image and spirit within the heart of man. Why don't we listen for that inner voice? It's God's voice that speaks through the heart to our subconscious minds. Why don't we learn to obey that good impulse at once and without hesitation? Good impulses are few and fleeting. If we don't act on them, if we postpone acting on them, they tend to wither and die. And as each dies, something of the finer person we might have been dies with it.

All of us have a compassionate urge, at one time or another, to do a good turn, say a kind word, or express an act of kindness toward another. But good intentions seldom are effective until acted upon. The road to hell is paved with good intentions, and tomorrow may be too late. We often stifle the generous impulse for fear of showing sentiment. Or we say, I'll do it later. The urge is lost and gone forever. Why not listen to your heart and obey that good impulse immediately? Unless you do, it's ten to one the good deed never will get done.

All about us there are thousands of persons with problems and physical needs. But there are millions of others who hunger mainly for those intangibles that money cannot buy. There is always the need for a heart-warming smile, a kindly voice, a friendly face, a pat on the back. It's up to you to listen to your heart, to find and do your part to help God write the music of our lives.

God has a purpose for every life. God, unquestionably, has a chore for each of us. Either we find and do our part, or it may never get done. To the extent that you and I fail, we delay by that much bringing the spirit of the Kingdom of Heaven down to earth.

Once a discouraged friend asked Will Rogers, "Will, if you had but forty-eight hours to live, how would you spend them?" "One at a time," was the ready reply. Will Rogers was a human philosopher who found contentment and happiness doing his work with confidence and cheerfulness and without worry. Listening to his heart, forgetting self and helping others, he kept time to the melody of the universe through humor.

One of the most confusing freaks of human nature is our tendency to be negative. We bemoan our lack rather than feel thankful for our luck. Man creates his own heaven and hell right here on earth. By constantly thinking and talking about our problems, we increase their weight if not their number. When we listen to our heart and count our blessings, we magnify and multiply them.

Why can't we learn to live with ourselves and our neighbors? Why do so many choose to dwell down in the dumps when the mountaintop view is so close at hand? Your pot of gold may be closer than you think. Why not look where it most likely can be found—at the end of your own rainbow? Learn to look for your bluebird of happiness in your own back yard.

When doubts and fears and tentions and bitterness assail you momentarily, don't panic. Relax! Remember the words of the lowly carpenter who said, "The Kingdom of God is within you." Listen to your heart. The Creator put His image and spirit in your heart. Get in tune with the harmony of God's universe. Listen to your heart. Relax!

LIVING FOR OTHERS ENRICHES YOUR LIFE

A small boy, when told "We are here in this world to help others," wanted to know, "What are the others here for?" The most unselfish man that ever lived was the most relaxed. Asking nothing for self, he spent his days upon this earth in service to others. Always blessings followed in his wake. He never raised his hands against his neighbor. Instead, he kept them ever ready to help and bless all men.

In a survey conducted some years ago, the question was asked, "Which man today has the best solution for the problems of the world?" The number one choice was the philosopher, doctor, musican, missionary, Dr. Albert Schweitzer. He lives only for others, was the reason given. By example he teaches his fellowmen to release the forces for good that are in all of us.

Doctors do not know the real causes of many of today's illnesses, but they suspect that anxiety, over-wrought nerves, and the feeling of being unloved and un-wanted are responsible for many maladies. Carl Jung, the great Swiss psychologist, said, "The central neurosis of our time is emptiness." Ernest Hemingway wrote be-fore he died, "I live in a vacuum that is as lonely as a radio tube when the batteries are dead."

Good sense and good judgment, plus experience, prove that in this world of gloom, tension, and despair, man needs to look outside himself toward others and upward to his Maker if his life is to be full and meaningful. "Only a man whose activity is directed by a great pur-pose can be fundamentally happy," said author William

Dean Howells. "Life is not a chase for personal happiness but is a field for endeavor toward the happiness of the whole human race."

"Loneliness," said Dr. Schweitzer, "is the most heart-rending anguish that bedevils the human race." He cautioned us to be ever alert to the needs of others. "Such a simple thing as a smile across the aisle of a crowded bus could be the spark of hope that prevents a suicide. Kindness is a form of philanthropy that is open to everyone. Many have discovered helping others to be the most enduring therapy, for it's the burdens you help another to bear that make your own seem light."

The greatest tension arena can be the home. What fools we are to lavish our most charming manners on outsiders and deny the simple, gracious courtesies at home to those dearest to us. Home is the place where tolerance and patience and concern for the feelings of others are most important. The home is the one place where loved ones should be most relaxed—together. But that does not mean we should forget to practice concern for others outside the home. Service to others, rather than emphasis on self, provides the key to success.

Truly successful men are not harried and driven. They are relaxed because they don't strive only for self. They have found time for civic enterprises and charities, devoting much of their time to the interest of others. Success is mostly psychological after all. It isn't merely wealth, power, education, or position—nor even the approbation of one's fellowmen. Success, that elusive quality imbedded in the state of the mind, comes to the man who learns to live, work, play, and think in terms of others.

Having unraveled this mystery of mysteries, success is truly ours. We no longer need seek what has already been attained. The secret of success is not a quality of exalted self but is to be found in one word—"others." We must learn this secret and practice it if we would relax and grow older gracefully. Why not make your influence count? Your influence can build up or tear down, spread joy or gloom, create harmony or discord, encourage evil forces or good, elevate or degrade, support ideals or weaken them. It's up to you. The social, moral, intellectual, and aesthetic climate is made by the influence we exert on the common life. So make some effort each day to be helpful. Because of what you do or say, or the way you act, the life of someone else can be different—and better.

GIVE—DON'T GRAB

Greed is a disease. Once the money-grabbing obsession takes possession of a covetous heart, rational behavior is doomed. Like Midas, the greedy grabber is never really satisfied. He craves more and more. The malady infests both the haves and the have-nots. The only difference is that one craves some; the other, more. This unnatural hunger causes men to lie, cheat, and steal. A greedy grabber takes all and gives nothing. Like a pond with no outlet, he becomes stagnant, slimy, and lifeless. He lives in an atmosphere of unrest and emptiness.

That nothing may be had for nothing is one of the immutable laws of God and man. Always the piper must be paid. We pay in labor, health, or sacrifice in other ways. The dreamer who drifts through life hoping to collect the rewards without making the payments is doomed to bitter disappointment. Greed imbedded in selfishness exacts a higher toll than any benefits derived.

There are enough of this world's goods for every man's need, but not for his greed. Life has many strange paradoxes, and one of them is "If you would be truly selfish, be generous." For there is no happiness in having or in getting, but only in giving. Giving pays better long-range dividends than grabbing. To keep the stream of life sweet and pure and wholesome, there must be circulation. There must be give and take, live and let live. Cynics to the contrary, experience has shown that it truly is more blessed to give than to receive. The secret of real happiness is not found in what can I get, but in what can I give, for the more you give the more you get to give.

It is not only more blessed to give than to grab, it is more profitable—*if*—you want and expect nothing in return. Otherwise, hypocrisy may seek to cover for greed. The secret is to be sure your giving is never tied in your mind with receiving anything in return.

No man can give away anything, anywhere, at any time, without eventually getting a greater return. Even when you give only a smile or a kind word, you get an inward pleasure and reward that far outweighs the effort it cost you. Give a beggar a dime for a cup of coffee and he warms his innards momentarily. But his look of gratitude can warm your heart with a million-dollar glow that lingers while memory lasts. And if his appreciation is sincere and deep, his own inner glow may outweigh and outlast any momentary physical satisfaction.

Giving not only keeps our souls green but makes us truly rich. If, as Dr. Schweitzer said, "giving is good exercise for our souls," then when in doubt give for your soul's sake, if not for the cause. The man is poor indeed whose heart has not been quickened by some little gift of himself. For no one has ever discovered a keener happiness than giving pleasure to others. And he who waits until asked to give has waited too long. In an attitude of gratitude our checkbook can be a series of thank-you notes to God for giving us enough and more than our needs.

Your example could cause another to listen to his own heart and give. This is one area where, to paraphrase Alfred Tennyson, "His echoes roll from soul to soul." "Giving calls for genius," said the Roman poet Ovid. "The only true gift," said Emerson, "is a portion of thyself." "If you want real happiness," said Dr. Schweitzer, "do something each day for which you get no pay—except the privilege of doing it." And never forget that you can't help anyone up the hill without getting closer to the top yourself. When you give *of* yourself, you give *to* yourself. Give of yourself often enough and goodwill come to you in many ways, including the relaxed spirit.

LIE DOWN IN PEACE AND SLEEP

One of the most vexing tension problems of our civilization is insomnia. We go to bed too late, overtired or overstimulated. Instead of being relaxed and prepared to rest and sleep, many of us crawl into bed only to review all the irksome problems of the day and anticipate those of the morrow. Resigned to another night of sleeplessness, we lay aside our clothes but not our cares, to face another restless, sleepless night of mental torment in which there can be little relaxation, peace, or refreshment.

How can any poor sleeper get the sleeping habit? The

best answer certainly is not in drugs, pills, or tranquilizers. Medications attack the symptoms, not the causes. To find peace of mind during the day and restful sleep at night, you must first learn to live with yourself and relax. You can sleep at night if you'll do these four things:

1. *Go to bed expecting to sleep.* Change your attitude. Stop telling yourself you can't sleep.

2. *Carry your problems only until sundown.* Do your best during the day and then refuse to think about problems until the next morning. Relax and rest at night. If you carry a load on your back all day, refuse to carry that load in your mind all night.

3. *Ask yourself why you can't sleep.* When you diagnose your own condition, the problem is already half solved. To sleep is to do what comes naturally. If it is because you're wound up from the problems of the day, you need to unwind at night. It can be with a good book, good music, friends and family, or even some TV. Then, at bedtime, off to sleep.

4. *Be your own doctor.* Having found the cause of your not-sleeping habit, correct it. It's as simple as that. Failure to sleep is due to a physical, mental, or spiritual cause, or perhaps to a combination of all three. Physical causes are easily spotted and should be easily remedied. Even these become chronic problems if allowed to persist.

Too tired to sleep? Physical or mental exhaustion calls for quiet reading, soft music, or a warm bath. If you're just not sleepy, cultivate the habit of going to bed at a regular hour—*expecting to sleep.* But when you just can't sleep, it's useless and stupid to lie there and toss. Do something about it. Go to the kitchen, drink a glass of milk, and go right back to bed and to sleep. Or watch late TV, memorize a bit of verse, or read until you feel sleepy, no matter how late. The important thing is to avoid the habit of not sleeping.

If you feel physically tense, exercise can provide a bedtime change of pace that can aid relaxation. If you still tend to roll and toss instead of sleep, get up to make sure the room is well ventilated and that cover is ample. If still sleepless, you might resort to a combination of physical, mental, and spiritual exercise. It seldom fails.

Three physical exercises I use in an emergency are simple ones I picked up years ago that I find effective.

The first is to stretch out at full length on your back, head back, and literally slump down into the bed, with no pressure anywhere and with every muscle completely relaxed, closing your eyes tightly, expecting to go off to sleep quickly. Remain quiet until sleep comes.

If this doesn't work shortly, add this breathing exercise. Take a deep breath, then expel most of the air from your lungs until you are almost wholly breathless. Then draw in fresh air until your lungs are completely filled, hold it briefly, then let it rush and then seep out. Breathing will soon be back to normal, and your body should become relaxed and drowsy. Now relax and off to sleep.

If more exercise is indicated, lie flat on your back, stretch the toes of both feet toward the foot of the bed as far as possible, then push both heels down to meet them until it hurts. Then wiggle your toes, ankles, knees, and hips. Then extend your arms, palms downward on the bed beside you, with fingers stretched as far as possible toward the foot of the bed. Wiggle your fingers, knuckles, wrists, elbows, and shoulders, ending by rolling your head several times in an easy circular motion, and forcing several yawns.

With a little practice anyone can learn to yawn. It's an

excellent exercise to help you relax when tired and tense. You can yawn at any time by opening your mouth wide, throwing your lower jaw into a free, relaxed position, and then rolling your lower jaw rapidly from side to side, at the same time drawing air deep into your lungs. Repeat the process a few times. Take a few more deep breaths. Soon yawning will become automatic at your wish. It's most relaxing. Try it now. Then practice it when needed as an aid to sleep.

If you still simply can't sleep, get up and do something else until you're ready for bed. Don't settle for failure in this area any more than you would in a business deal. It's mind over body, or vice versa. Don't encourge the nonsleeping habit another night. Determine to go to sleep, or get up. Go to sleep by sheer force of will, if need be, until sleeping automatically becomes a habit.

If physical exercises fail to work, try mental exercise. Just as men during the day, through courage and persistence, drive out fear with faith, you can use memory at night to subdue and drive out problems or negative thoughts by substituting positive and cheerful thoughts.

We know that most of the causes of insomnia are mental. And we know they generally spring from two sources of emotional tension, the most common of which is worry and the most insidious of which is resentment. Worry over problems, fancied or real, is rampant. All worry is useless and harmful. It is most vicious at night when you are ready for sleep. To carry problems and resentments to bed with you not only invites insomnia but is emotional suicide.

Try memory. Call to mind, in review, any of your favorite verses. If you don't have any memorized, get up and memorize some choice poem or quotation that inspires you.

Try reading. Get up and read a good book. Better still, read the Good Bóok. If its soothing messages seem to put some to sleep in church, why shouldn't it work at bedtime? Try browsing in Psalms 1, 8, 19, or 23. Read the wisdom of Solomon in Proverbs. Read Matthew 5–7, the Sermon on the Mount, frequently spoken of as the world's greatest speech. And "let not your heart be troubled."

Finally, if these mental and physical exercises fail to do the trick, then, as a last resort, you can always try prayer. Here, as always, we're prone to put off the most important until last. The proper kind of prayer would probabaly have made the other exercises unnecessary. Prayer soothes the spirit, calms the nerves, and creates an atmosphere of peace of mind and heart conducive to sleep. Religion, not tranquilizers, is the ultimate answer to insomnia. A prayerful attitude is the proper approach to all of man's problems—including insomnia. Prayer helps a man lay his burdens down, unwind, and relax. And until he relaxes, there can be little of sleep, or rest, or refreshment, or peace.

Good luck and good sleeping to anyone who has been troubled with sleeplessness. May you lie down each night, hereafter, content, to relax and sleep, and may you awaken each morning refreshed in body, mind, and spirit.

BEATING THE ULTIMATE TENSION

As head of Washington's Dale Carnegie school, my voice was perhaps my greatest asset. I had told thousands that a man's voice and personality are his fortune. I had successfully shown many national business and government leaders the proper approach to personality problems, and our class rooms taught the proven Carnegie methods of getting along with people.

Including my work as president and business manager of the school, for ten years I had held four jobs simultaneously. I designed, sold, and installed machine accounting systems to the federal government. I was executive vice-president and general manager of a pioneering hospitalization insurance company, as well as the chairman of its claims committee. I was also the principal officer of a real estate, financial, and educational corporation. I was busy day and night with duties and schedules and difficulties. As president of the Leadership Training Institute of the District of Columbia, I headed one of Dale Carnegie's largest schools in adult education.

Under the pressures of successful overachievement, my own attitude deteriorated, while I continued to emphasize the proper attitudes to thousands of others. It was a classic case of "Do as I say, not as I do." I grew less and less approachable and more and more irritable under the tensions of my demanding schedule. I became nervous and jumpy, which is hardly surprising in view of my work load. Maybe I thought I was a superman. Looking back, I realize I was a misguided, egoistic fool.

One day in 1952 the roof fell in. I had had a hacking cough and my voice had assumed a raspy, abrasive quality, which grew worse under friction and tension. I discovered I had cancer of the throat. An operation was recommended, with only one chance in seven of survival if I submitted, and an estimated six months to live if I did not. Under this hammer blow I reexamined my life and my attitudes. My doctor indicated that my trouble had been caused by a combination of tension, frustration, and worry.

First, I made my decision and vetoed the operation. Seven to one did not seem good enough odds. I took no medication, for the simple reason that medical science could offer none. If I only had six months to live, I knew I must put each precious moment to the maximum use. I had been given the most frightening news of my life, but I still was alive and I still had hope—and I still had faith. I did not simply give up. More important, I did not allow myself to become bitter.

As I have indicated throughout this book, when confronted with almost any problem there are the alternatives of acceptance or change—and change means the substitution of good habits and attitudes for bad ones. When you think you have only a few months to live, you realize how unimportant petty problems you worried about really are.

The nights were the worst. My sleep was constantly interrupted by near strangulation. Finally I discovered that the fumes of tincture of benzoin from a humidifier provided some relief. During the day I found that old-fashioned horehound candy, remembered from my childhood, relieved my coughing.

But tincture of benzoin and horehound candy only provided relief, not a cure. I was cured by something stronger than material things. I was healed through faith and prayer. Not a prayer that I would get well, but a prayer of apology, repentance, and resignation. I asked nothing for myself. I can recall no prayer that I get well, no plea to be cured, no asking for an extension of time beyond the estimated few months I had.

I prayed for my family, for friends, for enemies, for all

mankind. And I prayed for forgiveness for my own many shortcomings. I had no long-range hope, I made no long-range promises. I begged God to use the husks of my life according to His will. I was resigned, at peace, ready for whatever came.

Instead of dying, I gradually improved. Aided by prayer and my new attitude and renewed faith, after each near strangulation I'd get my head and throat clear of secretions and in utter exhaustion I'd fall back on my pillow, relieved and relaxed, to sleep soundly the rest of the night. In the morning I'd awake refreshed in body, mind, and spirit. I'd find my tensions had subsided, and for days my throat and voice would be stronger. And I was stronger in the certain conviction that I had walked and talked with God.

Gradually my strangling and choking ceased in the night as I began to relax more and sleep right through the night. Soon I would speak again, and even sing. Today I'm reminded of my weak throat only in rainy or inclement weather. I can't sing very loud or very well anymore, but my heart sings in gratitude to the friends who rallied around to help me run my business when not only my voice but my hope was almost gone.

During those long, painful nights of choking, of sleeplessness, of soul searching and meditation, I talked to the Lord with increasing frequency and clarity. He spoke to my heart, and as surely as I now live He speaks to me today. I spend each day and each night relaxed and without a care. During the night thought messages sometimes come to my subconscious with such force that they wake me. When they do, I reach for my pad and pencil, jot down a few notes, and drop right back to sleep. I awake in the morning refreshed in body, mind, and spirit.

From my own experience I sincerely believe that the right kind of prayer can cure any malady or illness, although I have the highest respect for the indispensable medical profession. I've had a really great doctor as my personal physician for years. Yet, were I again forced to choose between surgery and prayer, I'd again bet my life on the therapeutic power of prayer. Someday men and women will understand and realize their spiritual potential. One day mankind will discover the great secrets of the Spirit. When this breakthrough takes place, it will be the most revolutionary discovery in the history of man.

These secrets of inner space can be more meaningful than those discovered by our astronauts. Release of the secrets and power of the Spirit could be more far reaching than atomic energy or the secrets of outer space. When man learns to conquer inner space, to understand and control his own heart, mind, and spirit, he'll no longer be as baffled by the mysteries of the universe.

Since I took God as my partner for life, in all things, I have no real problems or fears. I cannot fail. I live on borrowed time, only to do His will as it is revealed to me. Whatever comes I shall accept as His will for my life. After God gave back my voice He put it in my heart to write a book to help others relax. So strong was the urge that it became almost a compulsion, as if by divine guidance I must share some of these very personal experiences with others. Twenty years later—this book is the result. I sincerely pray that it will help you to relax and live a more meaningful life.